FORAGING MEDICINAL HERBS AND WILD EDIBLE PLANTS IN THE GREAT LAKES REGION

Upper Midwest and Ontario —
Identify, Harvest, Prepare and Store Wild Foods
and Healing Herbs and Plants

Written by SAMANTHA DEERE

LEAFinPRINT

www.LEAFinPRINT.com

Foraging Medicinal Herbs and Wild Edible Plants
in the Great Lakes Region

ISBN: 978-3-907393-20-8

Contents

Recipes for your Wild Harvest

FREE GIFT TO OUR READERS
Cook with Medical Herbs and Plants

Integrate healing plants and herbs in your daily routine
Get 20 free recipes on how you can use the herbs and
plants presented in this book for cooking.

SCAN ME

or request by writing to: info@leafinprint.com

GET MORE IN-DEPTH KNOWLEDGE ABOUT MEDICINAL PLANTS & HERBS

From the same author

Herbalist's Guide to Native American Remedies

Medicinal Plants and Herbs, Powerful Herbal Traditions and Remedies for your Effective Home Apothecary Table

Check HERE:

www.leafinprint.com

or directly on Amazon:

https://www.amazon.com/Herbalists-Native-American-Remedy-Guide/dp/3907393015/ref

SCAN ME

STRESS RESILIENCE WORKBOOK WITH SEASONAL HEALING HERBAL INFUSIONS

16 Tools for Balanced Health & Focused Energy through Nutrition Matching your Body Type & Mindfulness Practice

Breathe a stress-free life. This book is full of actionable advice to help you balance your seasonal body reactions, break the stress cycle, and achieve true positivity.

The keys lie within yourself – understanding your body's natural rhythms and learning to work with them.

SCAN THE CODE to buy on Amazon

CHECK OUR WEBSITE: www.leafinprint.com

OR WRITE US : info@leafinprint.com

SCAN ME

1   Introduction

1.1   How to Use This Book

Simply put, foraging is the identification and harvesting of wild foods. Depending on who you talk to, foraging has different definitions. It begins with the intention to resonate with and respond to an ecosystem. The intention becomes an adventure, born from the curiosity to try something new. Even finding and chewing on one leaf is enough to satisfy! The experience is so direct and immediate. For the beginner, nothing more is required. Over time, the practice of foraging itself will be your guide. You will discover possibilities wherever you find yourself.

Some consider foraging a duty to prepare and consume food with the least amount of commercial impact on the planet. In the strictest sense, however, living off nature is quite difficult for most. Start small and keep things simple! Indeed, we can find foraging treasures in our backyards! Native American healers have pointed out that the plant capable of healing a person's condition usually is growing within fifty feet of their own home. How is this possible? It is as if the plant world understands what we need before we do. Learning how to forage teaches you that the natural world is guiding us and interacting with us all of the time.

What we seek is not so deeply hidden; it is right before our eyes in so many cases. Following the modest suggestions in this book will help you gain the assurance that the exciting world of wild harvesting has been patiently waiting for you. Surely, your adventures will yield great results.

The aim of this book is to:

- Develop your basic foraging skills and provide resources for more advanced foraging ventures.

- Help you create your own fun foraging excursion or vacation in the Great Lakes area with loved ones.

- Create delicious meals with your precious wild harvest.

- Learn ways to heal minor illnesses that you and your family experience with wild herbs and plants.

- Recognize and honor the origin of foraging practices in this country and become more aware of the traditions of the indigenous people in the Great Lakes region.

This book contains a very straightforward approach for the beginner. It introduces you to the unique characteristics of foraging in the Great Lakes region. The great lakes are Lake Superior, Lake Ontario, Lake Huron, Lake Michigan, and Lake Erie. They border eight US states (Illinois, Indiana, Michigan, Minnesota, New York, Pennsylvania, Ohio, and Wisconsin) and the Canadian Province of Ontario (see map below). The region was chosen as one foraging region since it lies in one climatic zone of warm-temperate continental climate[1] while being influenced by the climate effect of the lakes. Additionally, due to climate, altitude and geological history similar soil types and eco-zones developed[2].

Map US states and the Canadian province
of Ontario bordering the great lakes.

---

1   Köppen Climate Classification System, see for example: *https://www.nationalgeographic.org/encyclopedia/koppen-climate-classification-system*

2   *https://www.epa.gov/eco-research/ecoregions-north-america*

Armed with your trusty guidebook and the plant identification app this book recommends, you'll proceed. Vitally, this book provides a teaching guide on poisonous plant identification and botanical characteristics. From the beginning, understand the basic plants that you should not pick, and review the characteristics poisonous plants have. Then, look at the list of items you'll need for foraging – they are easy to procure and soon you will be on your way.

But what will I do with what I find?

Good question, the answer is in the Materia Medica section full of advice on not only the characteristics of forty-six plants but their edible uses as well. You'll find several possibilities to make an entire meal if you so desire. Would you like to use your harvest to feed your friends? We'll show you how to do that as well. The Materia Medica contains some of the more common herbs that both Native populations and settlers utilized. However, it teaches readers some of the lesser-known wild treasures of the Great Lakes region. The recipes invite curiosity and give readers an urge to start searching.

Next, we review harvesting and preparation methods for the plant parts you'll find including greens, shoots, stalks, nuts, and berries. Add barks, roots, and tubers found beneath the earth to your search and this completes a meal. Additionally, this book features a special section on harvesting seaweed. Seaweeds, when found in unpolluted areas, are a tremendous source of nourishment. The beauty of foraging around the Great Lakes is that your harvesting options increase, due to water plants.

Lastly, in order to connect you with the traditions of Native American foraging, we have provided a reference guide towards the end of the book so that you and your family can have a more direct experience with indigenous traditions if it suits you. Some of the Great Lakes tribes provide outreach opportunities for the general public to gain awareness of agricultural conservation and sustainable foraging practices. If you choose to visit one of the many state parks around the Great Lakes area, you can facilitate a superb foraging vacation. Lists of local conferences, food summits, and foraging courses will help you locate a knowledgeable forager in your area to take your journey further after you read this book. However, you must check local foraging laws through your Forestry Department or Parks and Recreation Department before you harvest in any location, whether it's in this book or not. Different rules apply to different locations discussed at the end of this book.

Now, let's begin with small and simple steps.

2 A History of Foraging in the Great Lakes Region

For thousands of years, foraging in native cultures was a way of life and constantly preoccupied communities. Our journey begins with a brief overview of some traditional Native American foraging practices and learning about their holistic life. From our vantage point, we can only try to become more aware of their traditions. We might wish to integrate these practices into our own modern lives with honor and respect. It is impossible to replicate the rich diversity of indigenous heritage in the Great Lakes and their forging traditions in the following section. This book is a small attempt, at best, to call attention to the indigenous origin of foraging practices.

2.1 Pre-Colonial Period (10,000 years ago)

Native Americans first came to the Great Lakes region via the land bridge from Asia. Estimates range from 10,000 to 15,000 years ago. At first, they lived and traveled primarily along water routes and water bodies. Yet by the 1600s they moved further inland.

One cannot generalize about tribal communities in any region. However, Great Lakes tribes had common features. Primarily they fell under the category of "Woodland" tribes. Woodland refers to North America's northeastern and southeastern woodlands. Tribes in these areas depended heavily on foraging in the forest in order to survive. Due to the diversity of the region, they had many options. They hunted, fished, gathered wild foods, and also had sustainable agriculture practices. Tribes in the southern states and southwestern states evolved to rely more on sustainable agriculture.

Great Lakes tribes, particularly in Wisconsin foraged wild rice as a staple food. In contrast tribes in other regions depended more heavily upon corn. Since sugar maples proliferated throughout the Great Lakes, native tribes developed complex sugar-making routines and extracted tree sap to make sugar during the spring. A more precise description of the sugaring process follows. However, due to the complexity of harvesting wild rice, for beginners, this book does not cover that topic.

Early accounts of earth-based tribal practices in the region exist. Archeologists have found signs of tribes thriving around the Great Lakes. For instance, on the shores of Lake Erie, images of tribal members smoking pipes were carved into rocks. Carvings depict medicine ceremonies, including serpents, feathers, and ritual articles made from leather. Other pictures show how indigenous people navigated the harsh landscape with snowshoes and trails. The pictures relay how the Erie Indians occupied the area and then went to war with the Iroquois, ultimately evacuating the area during the 17th century.

One way to simplify the networks of tribes that occupied the Great Lakes Region is that three primary tribes and eight secondary tribes formed the main subdivisions in the Pre-Colonial period. The primary tribes, Blackfoot, Cree, Kwakiutl, Micmac, Mohawk, Niska, and Ojibwa, had well over one thousand members each in the early 1600s. As the 1700s wore on the various tribal lineages decreased through foreign diseases, wars, and forced relocation.

However, the numbers of some of the main tribes in the Great Lakes Region eventually rebounded from decimation. Cherokee tribes in the late nineteen nineties reached three hundred and eighteen thousand members, while the Navajo tribes had two hundred and eighty thousand members. The 1990 census verified that over one hundred thousand members of the Ojibwa tribe had spread out, inhabiting federal reservations throughout Michigan, Wisconsin, Minnesota, and North Dakota. Currently, some of those reservations still exist and the tribes are striving to preserve their heritage. Some of them are listed in the reference section of this book (see Chapter 7 Foraging Locations and Learning Opportunities).

Briefly describing the foraging traditions of the Ojibwe woodland people of Northeastern America provides a place for us to begin imagining what foraging meant in earlier times. During the mid-seventeenth century, thirty-five thousand Ojibwa tribal members populated the continent. The seasons influenced all native tribes. Logistically, semi-nomadic Ojibwa tribes relocated to be nearer to food sources.

Just by looking at one tree, the Ojibwa harvested, we get an idea of how much they could utilize from a single source. Maple and birch trees were precious commodities. Maple yielded sugar, and birch provided materials for housing, canoes, and storage containers. Both Maple and Birch are profiled in the Materia Medica section of this book.

Maple was critical for sustenance. The Ojibwa widely used maple sugar or syrup to season their food. Understandably, they constructed villages close to maple trees. Every year they designated and marked the trees they would tap for sap. An astonishing number, sometimes up to 900 taps, yielded syrup for their tribe. They tapped the trees up to three times per year. They also rotated the groves they worked in from year to year so that the sap was replenished.

The Ojibwa poured the sap from birch bark containers into more substantial storage units constructed from moose hide, wood, or bark. Later, they traded for brass kettles to complete the lengthy sap boiling process. Storage was very important. They packed maple sugar into birch bark containers and hung it from the ceiling of their family dwelling. Other uses included pouring maple syrup right into the snow to make hard candy, a practice that is still popular today in various towns in the general Northeast.

Ojibwe tribes relocated to gardens and wild berry patches during the summer months. They grew corn, squash, and pumpkins and stored vegetables and seeds in pits under the earth during the fall and winter. Herbal teas sweetened with maple sugar and syrup were quite common. Otherwise, tribes fished or hunted throughout the year, drying and smoking their meats.

It is not unusual to find trails near areas where different tribes thrived, and one can try to walk, in a small way, in their shoes. To encapsulate their experience a Navajo prayer describes their authentic spirit of stewardship to the land. One may add here that this is the ideal picture. Later, we shall see a less than ideal one.

Maple syrup production in Quebec, Canada. Collecting maple sap in a traditional way.

Making sugar on snow, or maple toffee at the sugar shack in Quebec, Canada.

In beauty may I walk.
All day long, may I walk.
Through the returning seasons, may I walk.
On the trail marked with pollen, may I walk.
With grasshoppers about my feet, may I walk.
With dew about my feet, may I walk.
With beauty may I walk.
With beauty before me, may I walk.
With beauty behind me, may I walk.
With beauty above me, may I walk.
With beauty below me, may I walk.
With beauty all around me, may I walk.
In old age, wandering on the trail of beauty,
Lively may I walk.
In old age, wandering on the trail of beauty,
Living again, may I walk.
It is finished in beauty...
It is finished in beauty.[3]

---

3   Philip, Neil, ed.,"In a Sacred Manner I Live", from the *Nightway Chant* by Navajo Dine' p. 19.

As their culture diminished through foreign influence, foraging became a more suspicious activity than a sacred one. The next section addresses this.

2.2 The Colonial Period (1492-1776)

The Native American hunting and gathering traditions in the area could have left a vast legacy for foragers. Yet, most of this knowledge has been lost or dismissed. We can gather bits and pieces of the traditions, fortunately, preserved by individual authors and organizations. All Native tribes and their journey should be told. Yet unfortunately, due to space constraints, this book cannot cover the history of each tribe. Please refer to the resource section in this book for more resources (see Chapter 7 Foraging Locations and Learning Opportunities).

Research shows that tribes probably had to adapt their harvesting and foraging practices substantially during the Colonial period (ca. A.D. 1670–1783) and particularly before and beyond the Revolutionary War. They had to transition and relocate to keep their families safe from war and foreign diseases. It meant they farmed less and foraged more.[4]

2.3 Post Colonial Period (1776 through current times)

After the Revolutionary War, a cycle of tribal displacement became very common. Ultimately displacement culminated with federal laws that forbade foraging. States also adopted these laws, and many of these regulations still exist. Even as late as April of 2018, the National Park Service announced that they would *allow* a band of members from

---

4   VanDerwarker, Amber M. et. al, Farming and Foraging at the Crossroads: The Consequences of Cherokee and European Interaction Through the Late Eighteenth Century, Published online by Cambridge University Press: January 20, 2017.

the Eastern Cherokee tribes to forage a plant called Sochan in a major national park.[5] The Cherokee previously harvested Sochan freely yet responsibly. Sochan, at one time to the Cherokee, was like kale is for us today.

Literature about plants and their cultural uses is called ethnobotany. The academic study of ethnobotany did not even exist until the nineteenth century. Consequently, before the nineteenth century, no one was systematically recording indigenous plant utilization. Indigenous cultural traditions spread orally, from teacher to student and from generation to generation.

Reconstructing Native American foraging traditions is complicated by several factors. As mentioned, the traditions existed in oral rather than written form. Secondly, Sam Thayer, a master forager from Wisconsin, reminds us that historically, ethnobotanists often saw native traditions as foreign and savage and discredited their knowledge. They did not see the appeal of documenting their agricultural or foraging methods. Unfortunately, therefore, documentation is scanty.

By the 1800s and 1900s, European settlers had destroyed many tribes along with precious details regarding wild plant harvesting and usage. Increasingly, across disciplines, wild food became viewed only as survival food. Tribes became more dependent on mass-produced, prepackaged, staple foods. These choices did not contain the same nutritional components as a foraged diet. Meanwhile, only a fraction of the wild plants European peasants used became popular. The vast majority of plants tribes had foraged for hundreds of years were largely forgotten. Interestingly Thayer points out that today, the same handful of plants that European peasants used command most current literature on foraging. Consequently, this book contains many common herbs yet introduces some new ones.

Native Americans harvested bark, berries, roots, tubers, leaves, nuts, and seeds based on a seasonal calendar. They had no grocery store open

5   Linnekyn, Baylen, Complicated Rules For Foraging Aren't Helping Our National Parks (reason.com), *Reason Magazine*, April 6, 2019 Seen on April 1, 2022.

twenty-four hours a day. They had to plan, and they had to have reliable storage methods.

Today on some reservations, these methods are taught to a younger generation. On the White Earth Reservation in White Earth, Minnesota, the Ojibwe (Anishinaabe) have traditionally harvested rice, maple syrup, and berries. Their land covers 70,000 acres, and on it, they also hunt and fish. Despite health issues that plague the tribe due to consuming government foods the tribe has been forced to eat, they thrive. Activists are intent on helping members practice healthy and traditional methods of food consumption and foraging. Winona LaDuke (Anishinaabe, Ojibwe) stands out as one of the most well-known Native American activists. An environmentalist, economist, and writer, she established *Honor the Earth*, a nonprofit organization raising awareness and financial support for indigenous environmental justice. [6] Steadily the younger generations persevere, hopefully inspiring seekers to come.

This book is designed, quite literally, to give you a taste of the forager's beginning adventures. If you wish to take your foraging practices further, Sam Thayer's lifelong study of wild plants in the Great Lakes region is a superior resource. Additionally, you can review the reference section in this book to connect with resources that will help you forage wisely and authentically (see Chapter 7 Foraging Locations and Learning Opportunities).

Why, however, would a forager choose the Great Lakes region? Multiple factors make this area enticing. One is the mystique of the enormous bodies of water, their origins, and the habitat they create. Two is the variety of plant life in the area. Three is the history and the current foraging culture that exists and can guide the beginner. Let's explore some of these points.

---

6   Sorenson, Barbara Ellen, "Wild Food Summit: Anishinaabe relearning traditional gathering practices" *Journal of American Indian Higher Education,* February 15, 2011. Tribal College Journal

2.4 Myths and Facts of the Great Lakes

Your curiosity about foraging around the Great Lakes may bring you in touch with some fascinating stories, legendary accounts, and other journalist accounts of Great Lakes mysteries.

Many of the myths and legends of the Great Lakes Region are based on the oral traditions of the indigenous people. In current times, these stories, handed down and perhaps adapted, have fascinated many listeners.

Curiosity about the Great Lakes has often become sensationalized, as journalistic photographs and sometimes even videos show images that people cannot quite explain. They show creatures thriving in the deep waters, perhaps testing our faith in the supernatural. Are these stories true or false? Each of us has to assess these mysteries and determine whether or not they are true for himself or herself. However, even without sensational legends, the ancient aspects of the lakes alone are enough to captivate an audience.

Here are some fun facts about the mysterious watery realms:

- Lake Superior's Mishipeshu is an Ojibwe mythical water creature with the head and paws of an enormous cat, the horns of a bison, the scaly body of a snake, a spikey back, and a tail (see picture below) . Sightings of Mishipeshu have been reported in Lake Superior close to Michipicoten Island. The odd being is not particularly friendly. Legend has it that Mishipeshu can cause a storm.

- Like the Bermuda Triangle, Lake Michigan also has a triangular region known for its lost ships and airplanes. One of the first recorded disappearances occurred in 1881 when the boat *Thomas Hume* seemingly vanished into thin air. Was the cause a UFO? Was it a time travel portal? Or was it the weather? What do you think?

- In 2009 University of Michigan researchers discovered archaeological evidence of the presence of an advanced ancient civilization dating back to the 7th millennium BC just 100 feet below the surface of Lake Huron!

- Bessie of Lake Erie may perhaps be the most well-known lake creature. She is the cousin of Scotland's Loch Ness Monster. First reported in 1793, Bessie is described in many different ways but friendly to intruders.

Giant fish species such as the Northern Pike, the Muskellunge, and Lake Sturgeon inhabit the great lakes. All have a serpentine appearance and are incredibly long, the size of small dolphins. Could these appear to some as a monster? It is possible, and they are far more numerous than the mythical creatures.

The Mishibizhiw or Great Lynx and canoes and serpents are part of the Agawa Rock Pictographs. Rock art was created by the Ojibway people in the 17th or 18th centuries. The site is found in Lake Superior Provincial Park, Ontario, Canada.

Pike fishing. Fisherman catch fish in water at river.

Beneath the sensational, there is more profound regard that native tribes had for the water. Many native tribes believe that creation arose from the water. According to different legends, water spirits would mate with other gods on land. Their progeny became the heads of a tribe that grew over time. Fish from the lakes could therefore transform into partially human gods and could speak or communicate divine messages. Creation based on the water was such a fundamental belief that daily supplications given to the water played a role in sustaining all life. Traditional native chants honoring the water have a deeply soothing and profound quality; they are well worth taking a moment to hear on YouTube.[7]

---

7   Please see the following on YouTube: (1) Turtle, Alex, Diné (Navajo) and Southern Cheyenne, Chenoa Egawa, Lummi, and S'Klallam. "The Water Song" Seen on March 20, 2015: (366) The Water Song – Chenoa Egawa & Alex Turtle – YouTube – I would take it out. Good song but a bit out of context.

3 Geographic Features
Source (5)(8)(10)(13)

3.1 Great Lakes Area Geography

From their westernmost tip (Duluth, Minnesota) to easternmost point (Watertown, New York), the Great Lakes cover almost one thousand miles across the United States and Canada. The shoreline is 9,000 miles—longer than the U.S. East and Gulf coasts combined.

There are eight states included in the Great Lakes borders (Illinois, Indiana, Michigan, Minnesota, New York, Pennsylvania, Ohio, and Wisconsin) and the Canadian Province of Ontario (Please see the map below).

It is quite awe-inspiring when you see the endless horizon beyond the lake. The region holds the largest surface of freshwater worldwide – nearly 20% of the world's freshwater. The Great Lakes provides 10% of the total drinking water for the Americas.

More than 35,000 inland islands or groups of inland islands are located in the Great Lakes region. In the Canadian part of Lake Huron, for example, lies Manitoulin Island, the largest inland lake island in the world in terms of area, at 2,766 square kilometers.

Lake Huron and Lake Michigan are joined by a small point. Otherwise, the elevation between the lakes varies by 150 meters. Niagara Falls moderates the differences in height. Its waters plunge from Lake Erie to Lake Ontario and congeal into the St. Lawrence River.

However, most people in the great lakes live in a major city. What if you are based in an urban environment in the lakes area? Is foraging still possible for you? The answer is yes! There is a chapter in this book just dedicated to urban wild harvesting and you will find out what wild food the city can provide for you.

Map of the Great Lakes region showing states and provinces bordering the lakes and the main cities. The shaded regions around the lakes show their drainage basins and St Lawrece River that takes the lake water into the Atlantic Ocean.

Niagara Falls between Lake Erie to Lake Ontario cascade thirty-five thousand tons of water every five seconds.

3.2   Climate and Weather

Source (8)(13)

The lakes are a critical feature that guides the areas' weather patterns. The enormous Great Lakes act to absorb the heat of the lands surrounding them. The moderate temperatures cool areas down in the summer and create more warmth throughout the winter. The lakes transform into huge humidifiers, elevating the air's moisture content.

Winter months bring long nights and cold days to the Great Lakes Region. Over the winter, the additional moisture coming from the lakes turns into heavy snowfall that covers the regions close to the lakes. Residents call this "lake effect" snow. It occurs when cold winds flow over large lake areas with warm water in winter. Water vapor is picked up over the lake, but it quickly freezes and falls as snow on the shores and inland lake areas. The resulting Snow Belt extends across five states. Interestingly these vapors and waves from high winds flash freeze into incredible ice formations. The spontaneous ice sculptures provide winter entertainment for residents and visitors alike.

Spring brings a great thaw to the lakes. Both spring and autumn are foggy months along the shorelines, and the weather becomes unpredictable due to the interactions with large bodies of water. Currents and strong winds churn the lakes during spring. When the seas settle, the Soo Locks open so that commercial ships can finally pass from Lake Superior down to the other lakes. Summer is different, the nights become shorter, and the days become warmer.

3.3   Geology and Soils

Source (5)(14)

During the last ice age, which reached its peak about 21,500 years ago, the mile-thick Laurentide ice sheet covered most of Canada and the northern United States. This glacier's massive weight and movement gouged out the earth to form the lake basins. When the climate warmed, and the ice sheet retreated. Water from the melting glacier filled the basins forming the Great Lakes. Approximately 3,000 years ago, the Great Lakes reached their present shapes and sizes.

Varieties of sandstone and limestone include a frame around the southern lakes. Resistant strata composed of hard dolomite and soft shale stretch to the Niagara. We find that the same materials comprise the ancient Canadian Shield surfaces towards the Canadian border.

It is noteworthy that thirty-five percent of the salt used in the Americas comes from deep underneath Lake Huron, Lake Michigan, and Lake Erie. Below their depths lay salt caves protected from water by a rocky basin formed over millions of years. For example, Whiskey Island Cargill Salt Mine lies 1,800 feet under Lake Erie.

Unique Plant Species of the Great Lakes

A major asset when foraging near the lakes is discovering water-based plants and those based on the land. The Materia Medica contains a couple of water plants to discover! Otherwise, there are plenty of berries you can try, tubers, nuts, and of course, some spices and a lot of greens.

The Great Lakes created a climate that allowed marshlands, islands, forests, and the ecosystem of the water itself to develop. Therefore, trees and flowers thrive, and marshland grasses, reeds, and aquatic plants like seaweeds. The Great Lakes region features a large selection of wild berries. Berries grow in full sun yet also need substantial moisture. Inland regions provide both conditions, so it is not surprising that foragers can feast on wild berries. Like the Butternut or acorns described in the Materia Medica section, Nuts are typical. Fruits such as Persimmons and Paw Paws are possible to find. Altogether, this diversity has the potential to yield a forager's feast.

Plants channel their energy into different plant parts at certain times of the year, creating the distinct seasons in which various species appear. Regardless of specific dates, plants emerge and ripen in a predictable sequence. However, like those in the Great Lakes region, geographic specialties can alter the climate producing a *microclimate*. Shoreline plants often develop a week or two later because of shallow craters that remain free of water on the sandy soil. These 'frost pockets' create a miniature arctic climate as the cold air fills these pockets at night. Cooler temperatures prolong the growing season of certain plant species, such as fiddleheads. Shoot-bearing vegetation like cattails appear later, but you can harvest them for weeks longer than under normal conditions. Over time, a forager understands how to use a microclimate wisely to prolong the gathering of more plants of a particular type.

4   Getting Prepared to Forage

4.1   Urban Foraging

Source (1)(9)

Urban foraging has found its way to social media, amassing more than 70 million viewers. Followers are fascinated by foraging techniques that lead to food preparation alternatives. They are excited to add wild dandelions, acorns, or mushrooms to their daily table. The most populated cities in the Great Lakes Region are Toronto, Ontario (Canada), Mississauga, Chicago, Illinois, Milwaukee, Wisconsin, Hamilton, Cleveland, Ohio, Buffalo, and New York. These cities contain hidden opportunities to begin a forager's journey.

Current research by the US Forest Service supports harvesting wild food in public spaces, notably common plants and fungi. Urban foraging can contribute to supplying nutritious food supplements and may give different populations greater access to nutritional substances. Foraging can provide

- Provision for affordable food.

- Possibility of increasing nutrition.

- Supplements of dietary nutrition.

- An increase in urban land use awareness.

- An elevated understanding of alternative and complementary therapeutic options.

- Awareness of climate change through direct interaction with plants throughout different seasons.

It is important to note that most of these points apply to all foragers, not just urban seekers.

Urban foraging tips:

Urban foraging is more straightforward than one may think. There are some easy ways to get started. The first thing to do is to check the foraging regulations in your area by contacting the local Forestry Department or Parks and Recreation Department.

1. Consult a local field guide to learn what to find in your area.

2. Install a plant identification app on your phone (*iNaturalist on the App Store (apple.com) or iNaturalist on the google play App Store for your Android*).

3. Check for local foraging classes at your health food store, through Parks and Recreation Departments, or the local Forestry Department. Some classes are free or by donation.

4. Do not forage in high traffic or polluted areas.

5. Hunt in thickets, large parks, or small forested areas that are well lit, and not too secluded. Vacant lots or areas around schools are also possibilities.

6. Check land management websites before you get into trouble picking plants on privately owned property.

7. Lastly, become familiar with a seasonal foraging calendar so that when you find your favorite spots you'll know what to search for from week to week.

8. The rest of this book will still apply to those in urban settings. Your main challenge is to find legally available land, and competent foraging professionals to guide you.

4.2   The Fifteen Best Foraging Practices

Source (3)(4)(6)(10)

1. Foraging can be as simple as walking outside your front door, picking a handful of plantain leaves to subdue swelling from an

insect bite, and walking back into your home to apply them. Likewise, you might choose a rose or a common purple violet and put it in your mouth. Eating wild food is a natural instinct; our ancestors lived by foraging for thousands of years.

2. The supermarket, in historical terms, is a relatively new invention. Once you discover that what you once assumed was a weed can provide you with more nutrients than many items you consume, the magic of foraging will grip you. You may discover more than just a casual pastime. You might become more mindful of eating in harmony with the season. It may encourage you to think about why each plant becomes available at a specific time. Why? Inevitably one cannot help but become entranced by the essential elements, water, air, earth, sunlight, and wind. You will awaken your senses as you taste, touch, and smell everything. You will use your senses actively in the plant identification process. It is a new world.

3. The first step to foraging is to read this book. You can use a pocket field guide alongside the plant identification app on your phone. Seeing different accurate photographs of the plant will give you the confidence that you are making the right choice. It is essential for a beginner. The exciting thing is that once you recognize a plant even one time, you are far more likely to spot it again. You will begin to build a visual database of plants in your head. It is a delightful enterprise. Most beginner herb books contain the most common plants and herbs in the U.S. and Canada. You can collect more foraging books as your progress, and compare plant identification profiles, and materia medica.

4. Start in your backyard by witnessing the growth cycle of plants – first observe. When you just walk and watch what is around you without putting tremendous pressure on yourself to harvest something, you can simply learn how plants appear from season to season. What are their characteristics? How do plants behave?

5. Try to go on a couple of herbal walks per year with a seasoned professional. They will point out the most common plants in

your region. They will also advise you about common pitfalls you may encounter on your walks. National parks employees lead these types of excursions. On these nature walks, you will learn about some of the wild animals in your area and their habits. Forestry Department guides will help you identify plants on these walks. After identification, you can explore their edible and medicinal uses by looking at your herbal reference guides.

6. Connect to the library, local co-op, or natural food store in your area to learn about these walks or explore options online. There is a local reference section in this book for the Great Lakes Region for foragers, so you can begin exploring.

7. Start taking photos of plants and making a collection. You can also carry a small blank book with you, tape a leaf or flower inside the book as you explore, and take notes. Write down the plant's name next to each plant part you procure. Keeping a book will build your confidence and knowledge from adventure to adventure.

8. Take advantage of YouTube videos on specific plants. Search for the common or Latin name of the plant. Many knowledgeable herbalists online often produce a small documentary about a particular plant. It will include their personal experience as a practitioner using the plant, which is fascinating to learn about a specific herb. Bridgette Mars, Yarrow Willard, and Emily Ruff are excellent herbalists to watch. Adam Haritan, a botanist and naturalist, is another extremely knowledgeable forager.

9. First, learn to identify the plants growing in your backyard and neighborhood! You will discover the most amazing things close to your own home.

10. Set a goal to learn several different plants per year. If you learn step by step, it will not be too overwhelming. Remember that there is plenty that you can do with a few essential herbs, such as Mint, Yarrow, and Plantain.

11. Never use a plant until you are sure that you have identified it correctly. If you cannot be sure, do not use the plant.

12. Important: Once you have positively identified a plant to harvest, taste only a tiny amount of it first to ensure that you will not have an allergic reaction.

13. After identifying the plant, make sure that it is not an endangered species or a rare plant. There are always many other plants that can substitute for the one you seek. Special note: *Be careful of the carrot family hemlock; water hemlock and other family members are highly poisonous. Please learn to distinguish hemlock and water hemlock from elderberries. This book contains a section on common plant identification mistakes for you to consult.*

14. Do not harvest more than you plant to utilize. Follow the standard rule of never gathering more than one-third of the total available plant in the harvesting area. The rule ensures that the plant will be able to propagate and sustain itself.

15. Beware of harvesting from polluted areas such as along roadsides. Plants that grow along the road might be contaminated with benzene, lead, oil, and other pollutants from automobiles. If you harvest plants near farms, they may contain pesticides. Damp areas are populated with viruses, worms, Giardia, amoebas, and other forms that spread bacterial infections. Always wash whatever you forage, whether you cook it or not. Cook mushrooms for 25 minutes at least. Mushrooms attract more bacteria than most plants. One must eliminate contaminants through cooking.

4.3   List of Items for a Foraging Walk

You will need

1. Something to put your harvest in, like a basket or cloth bag

2. Several smaller bags to keep your items separate.

3. A pair of kitchen scissors to cut the more delicate leaves.

4. A substantial utility knife to harvest branches, bark, and sever the sturdier stems.

5. Your First Aid Kit for longer foraging excursions.

6. A couple of water bottles *always*.

7. Access to your phone's GPS or an area map is beneficial even if you think you know where you are going.

8. A jar for berries and a paper bag for mushrooms really help keep your produce whole and fresh.

9. Insect spray and sun protection.

10. Tick-proof clothing and spray if you plan to walk in tick-ridden areas.

If you forage for seaweed you will need

1. Waterproof boots and warm clothing during the colder season.

2. A hat for sun protection.

3. A pair of scissors.

4. A plastic bag to store the seaweed pieces.

5 Identification Methods for Harvesting Wild Plants

5.1 Basic Botanical Vocabulary with Plant Characteristics

Source (1)(5)(11)(4)

One must be sure about the identity of a plant before consumption. You are taking your own life and the life of others into your hands. Compare pictures of plants in this guidebook with your plant identification app. In particular, read the 'look alikes' section in this book, and other guides as well. Then triple check the plants' identity with a third source (triple check method). By the time you harvest and consume the plant, absolutely no doubt must remain that it is a suitable variety.

When looking at a plant, ask yourself the following questions:

- What is the plant type?
- In which location does it grow?
- Does it have a flower? What are its characteristics?
- How about bark or the stem structure?
- What type of texture does the plant or tree have?
- Which characteristics does the foliage display (leaf shape, margin, or vein)?
- What is the growth pattern of the leaves (for instance, alternate, opposing, etc.)?
- Does the plant or tree bear fruit?
- How do the seeds form, and what are their characteristics?

- Are there any other unique characteristics (for instance, color change in the fall or an adaptive feature)?

When looking at botanical guidebooks, the same botanical characteristics will appear in field guides over and over again.

1. **Alternate**: Leaves growing from opposite sides instead of being paired.

2. **Basal**: Growing from the plant base at or near ground level.

3. **Biennial**: A plant that usually has a two-year life cycle – The first year, it is without a stalk and displays a rosette. In the second year, it has a flowering stalk. After this, it generally dies.

4. **Bract**: A small modified leaf found directly beneath the flower or cluster

5. **Bulb**: A round growth beneath the ground that becomes enlarged to store the plant's energy.

6. **Channeled**: Grooves or depressions running the length are also called petioles.

7. **Colony:** A group of the same plant species grows together.

8. **Composite:** Clusters of many very tiny flowers that appear as one (e.g., Dandelion flowers).

9. **Compound leaves**: Consist of multiple leaflets connected by petioles, generally to a primary axis.

10. **Deciduous:** The process of dying and falling away at the end of a growing season.

11. **Dicot:** One type of flowering plant that has net patterned veins, a prominent central root, and two seed leaves (e.g., clovers, dandelions, strawberries, or maples)

12. **Fiddlehead:** The coiled shoot of a fern.

13. **Lanceolate:** Shaped like a lance head, pointed, long rather than wide, and located near the base.

14. **Leaflet:** One of the smaller leaves or blades within a compound leaf.

15. **Lobe:** a broader divine of a leaf rather than constricted (e.g., Oak leaves or Sheep Sorrel leaves).

16. **Margin:** The outside edge of a leaf. (e.g., Many leaves have serrated margins with tiny teeth.)

17. **Midvein:** The central vein of a leaf, sometimes called a Midrib.

18. **Monocot:** a flowering plant with parallel veins and without the central taproot that first germinates with a single leaf (e.g., onions and lilies)

19. **Mucilage:** A sticky or slimy substance indicting the presence of starches (e.g., purslane leaves are mucilaginous)

20. **Nodes:** The point on a stem that bears one or more leaves.

21. **Nutmeat:** The edible portion of a nut.

22. **Opposite:** Growing in pairs from the stalk on the opposite side. Also referred to as 'opposing.'

23. **Ovate:** Long and egg-shaped, with the broadest part near the plant's base. Sometimes this is referred to as 'oval shaped.'

24. **Palmate:** Hand-shaped or having several finger-like lobes

25. **Pedicel:** The stem of an individual flower or fruit with a cluster.

26. **Perennial:** A plant that lives for more than two years.

27. **Petal:** flower leaf

28. **Petiole:** The stem or stalk of a leaf.

29. **Pinnate:** Feather-like with leaflets, branches, or veins, arranged in two rows along opposite sides of the midvein (e.g., Ferns or Yarrow)

30. **Raceme:** a flower cluster in which each flower on a stem emanates from an elongated central stem

31. **Rhizome**: A horizontal stem of a perennial plant found underground with roots coming from the nodes.

32. **Root:** Roots anchor the plant underground and absorb its nutrients and water. They don't have leaves or buds.

33. **Rosette:** A circular cluster of leaves radiating from the same point, usually forming a crown at the root or base of a stem

34. **Sessile:** Attached directly, without a stalk or petiole.

35. **Shoot:** A fast-growing stem or stalk of the plant (e.g., asparagus)

36. **Simple:** Not compound, a single-leaf unit.

37. **Stamen:** The male portion of a flower that bears pollen. There are usually multiple stamens.

38. **Succulent:** Refers to a juicy, thick, and fleshly plant.

39. **Taproot:** A primary central root that grows directly downward rather than horizontally.

40. **Tuber:** An enlarged stem that stores energy, mainly in the form of starch.

41. **Umbel:** A flower cluster in which all of the stalks radiate from the same point.

42. **Vein/Rib:** Integral part of plants and act as a medium to transfer minerals and nutrients in leaves. The 'nerve' of a leaf.

43. **Wholed/ verticil:** Arangement of leaves, sepals, petals, stamens, or carpels that radiate from a single point and surround or wrap around the stem or stalk.

5.2 Identifying Poison Plants

Source (1)(7)(11)(14)

Always keep the number of a poison control center in your wallet and your car.

Some characteristics are common among poisonous plants. Learn these characteristics and let them serve as a guide. However, do not rely upon them entirely. Follow the triple check method in the foraging tips section of this book that veteran foragers generally advise. If you have the slightest doubt whether or not a plant is poisonous, do not even touch it.

Signs of a possibly poisonous plant include:

1. Milky sap

2. Plants that do not taste good (perhaps beyond your typical bitter – extremely bitter or caustic)

3. Naturally shiny leaves

4. Plants that produce yellow or white berries

5. Umbrella-shaped plants

6. Assume a mushroom is poisonous until you can safely and positively identify that it is edible.

ThThis list gives first-hand guidance but is not exhaustive.

If you decide to harvest seaweed make sure that the area you forage is not contaminated by industrial waste or pesticides from farms that are close to the site.

Here is a partial listing of poisonous plants that look similar to plants that are not poisonous. Learn to identify these plants before your first foraging outing. It is best to understand what to avoid first and which poisonous plants often harm unaware harvesters.

Practical on your phone – Get color pictures of the 17 poisonous plants and 45 Edible and Medicinal Herbs presented in this book

If you read the black and white version of this book, you can get the full-color pictures of all herbs and plants presented here.

For most people, colored images facilitate the identification of plants. Simply scan the QR code below to access the download directly.

If you prefer getting them as a pdf on your computer, just drop us a mail at info@leafinprint.com.

1 – The Hepatica family

Hepatica Americana (American Liverwort)

The hepatica family emerges in early spring. Some varieties have kidney or liver-shaped leaves with hairy petioles. Other varieties have small fan-shaped leaves, separated into swords. The plant contains burning alkaloids and is very poisonous.

2 – Arrow Arum

Peltandra virginica

An arrow-shaped leaf with pinnate veins that grow in the water. The plant is bitter, and all parts, including the flower and mature fruits, are poisonous.

3 – Bloodroot

Sanguinaria canadensis

The underground rhizome leaks a red sap when broken. The leaves have deep dissections and a single white flower. The plant's juice will burn the skin and eyes; eating even a tiny portion of the plant can be fatal.

4 – Blue Flag Iris

Iris spp[8].

Sword-like leaves; purple, yellow, blue flowers with rhizomes. It will cause diarrhea, vomiting, and dermatitis.

5 – Death Camas

Zigadenus venenosus

Deeply dissected, carrot-like leaves, white flowers look like 'bloomers' or breeches. The tuber is poisonous and causes convulsions and breathing difficulties, yet it is rarely fatal.

---

8   The abbreviation, spp, is botanical shorthand for multiple species.

6.1 – Poison Sego

Cycad Sago

All parts of the *sago* palm are *poisonous*, but the seeds (nuts) are the most *toxic* to pets.

Not to be confused with saw palmetto

7 – Hellebore, False

Veratrum viride

It grows in wet swamp areas and has large ovate leaves without stalks that climb upwards, bearing yellow-green flowers. Causes asphyxia, convulsions and death.

8 – Horse Nettle

Solanum carolinense

Spiny stems and leaves have a coarse texture. White flowers and a fleshy yellow berry cause nausea, vomiting, and stomach and bowel pain.

9 – Mayapple

Podophyllum peltatum

This woodland plant is leaf-shaped like an umbrella with deep dissections. Flowers are single white or yellow, and there is a green fruit. Ingesting may lead to coma and death.

10 – Nightshade, Bittersweet

Solanum dulcamara

A climbing vine with purple rocket-shaped flowers that bear an orange-reddish fruit – Leaves are lobed and alternate. It causes nausea but is not usually fatal.

11 – Poison Hemlock

Conium maculatum

The stems have purple spots. Large white umbels with many-branched flower heads arise from the stem. This plant is a must-learn look-alike for other wild species such as the wild carrot, wild anise, wild parsnips, and other carrot family members. Ingestion leads to respiratory failure and death.

12 – Poison Ivy

Toxicodendron radicans

It can appear as a climbing vine or shrub. One must learn about this plant because the consequences of having poison ivy are genuinely unpleasant and painful. Leaflets come in threes. Berries are white or pale yellow. Contact results in dermatitis, sometimes severe. Learn wild plants like jewelweed, plantain, and purslane that can soothe poison ivy immediately after you contact it.

13 – Poison Oak

Toxicodendron diversiloba

A small shrub looks like poison ivy, but the leaves have deeper lobes. It causes contact dermatitis.

14 – Poison Sumac

Rhus vernix

It is not Red Sumac – This plant has white fruits rather than red and is shrub-like with compound leaves and seven to fifteen leaflets. It causes contact dermatitis.

15 – Pokeweed

Phytolacca americana

Pointed ovate leaves join to reddish-purple stems. It has clusters of deep purplish-black berries. It grows on wastelands. Consumption causes cramps and vomiting but is rarely fatal.

16 – Skunk Cabbage

Symplocarpus fortidus

It is a primitive, fleshy wetlands plant. When broken, it emits a skunk-like smell. It is bitter, and the juice causes a terrible burn, but it is not fatal.

17 – Water Hemlock

Cicuta maculata

A wetlands plant that has sharply toothed leaves and bears the resemblance of poison hemlock. Again, it is worth revisiting the deadly look-alikes to the wild carrot family. Death can occur after only a few hours of consuming this plant.

5.3   Suggested Guidelines for Food Poisoning

Please note: Always keep the number of a poison control center in your wallet and your car. Call them immediately if you suspect that you or someone you know has food poisoning.

5.3.1   How do I know if I have food poisoning?

According to the CDC (Centers for Disease Control), food poisoning symptoms include severe nausea, stomach cramps, diarrhea, and vomiting; however, you can have more severe symptoms such as slurred speech, droopy eyelids, weakness, rashes, or a loss of balance. The critical difference between stomach flu and food poisoning is that the ***symptoms come on much faster.*** In mild cases, food poisoning should not last more than 48 hours. If it does, seek medical attention immediately. Food poisoning can lead to chronic health disorders such as reactive arthritis and chronic immune deficiency, or even death in severe cases.

5.3.2   Natural Remedies

**Please note that those over 65 years old, those under the age of 5 years, those with previous immune conditions, and pregnant women are most susceptible to food poisoning. This protocol is unsuitable for pregnant women. Activated Charcoal is contraindicated for pregnancy. Enemas are not safe for pregnant women either and can lead to miscarriage. If you are pregnant and have food poisoning, contact emergency medical support immediately. This protocol is not suitable for children. Again, contact poison control and emergency medical support.

For mild cases (with improvement within 48 hours), the goals of the following natural healing essences and guidelines are to:

1. Reduce harmful bacterial levels.

2. Remain adequately hydrated and restore electrolyte balance.

3. Heal the stomach and intestines.

4. Reduce diarrhea and stomach/intestinal cramping.

Again, if you are insecure or your gut feeling tells you something is wrong, seek medical advice. Better safe than sorry.

Oil of Oregano

Oil of Oregano is one highly concentrated essential oil that is safe to ingest a couple of drops at a time. *Most essential oils are not food grade.* Oregano oil is one you can find that is safe to consume. It is a remedy to always keep on hand. You will have to follow the number of drops recommended on the vial. They come in various sizes. However, you will take this natural form of an antibiotic four times daily.

Psyllium Powder

Take one teaspoon of Psyllium powder three times daily. It will absorb toxicity. Reduce the dose to two times daily if you start to become constipated.

Activated Charcoal

Always keep Activated Charcoal pills on hand. However, *only* take them for specific purposes. Activated Charcoal is powerful and expands to 300 times its size, and absorbs toxins very effectively, also incredibly stubborn ones. Never, ever take it long-term.

Upon the first signs of food poisoning, take five tablets. After six hours, take another five pills. At this point, one should see a marked improvement from this short-term treatment.

Additional Natural Remedies

If you are not in a hygienic environment and feel signs of either food poisoning or flu, eat something, take two Garlic tablets (or two fresh cloves of Garlic chopped) and consume probiotics to combat the effects of what you ingest. Symptoms will reduce.

Herbal Tea for Diarrhea and Cramping

Astringent herbs stop diarrhea in many cases. To prevent cramping, take an antispasmodic herb.

Combine one tablespoon of fresh grated Ginger (antispasmodic) with one tablespoon of an astringent – either Yarrow leaves, Chamomile aerial parts, Meadowsweet aerial parts, or Plantain leaves in 1 quart of boiling water. Let this steep for 15 minutes—strain into a glass jar. Take three cups daily.

5.3.3 Diet

Remember the BRAT diet: Bananas, Rice, Apples, Toast

For the first three days or more, you will eat several small portions of bland foods daily. Give your stomach a rest. Consume low-fat foods that do not strain the digestive system.

Chicken, vegetable broth or bone broth, bananas, rice porridge (refer to the Rice Porridge/Congee recipe under the IBS protocol, egg whites, mashed potatoes, or mashed avocados (mashed avocados replace electrolytes relatively quickly).

Honey can be a very healthy way to restore balance, and it acts medicinally.

When you start to heal, introduce or reintroduce probiotics into your diet. Begin with yogurt or Kefir, which will help soothe and coat the stomach and reduce acidity; try a Tablespoon at a time of kombucha, and try Miso Soup as a plain nourishing broth probiotic.

Hydrate and replace your electrolytes. Don't become dehydrated! Do not attempt to eat solid foods too soon – Allow your stomach and intestines to rest – Avoid sports drinks like Gatorade to combat dehydration. These will only worsen your diarrhea – Completely avoid alcohol, soda, sugary drinks, heavy carbohydrates, fried foods, nicotine, and spicy foods.

Coconut water hydrates quickly.

Lemon water with honey/maple syrup and a dash of salt (Himalayan salt is best because it contains the most nutrients) is an excellent way to hydrate. In countries where it is scorching, this is often sold as a street beverage to prevent heatstroke.

Sources

(1)   Cornell University College of Agriculture and Life Sciences "Plants Poisonous to Livestock and Other Animals" Cornell University Department of Animal Science

(2)   Blakley, Natasha, Great Lakes Now, Meet the person making Great Lakes ice popular on TikTok – Great Lakes Now, April 1, 2022

(3)   Dabadie, Sabine, and Phillip B. Stark, The Berkeley Food Institute, "Urban Foraging In Municipal Public Parks and Public Schools: Opportunities for Policy Makers," July 2017

(4)   Day, Doreen, Waubay Newquay, Marten Clan, "The Water Song," composed by Mashkoonsee Day, Warsaw Wahzoo Banaise Dodgem (Condor Clan) (366) The Water Song – YouTube

(5)   Great Lakes Today, Seen on: (*https://www.greatlakestoday.org/post/video-salt-mine-lies-1800-feet-under-lake-erie*)

(6)   Falconi, Diane, Wendy Hollender Illus., "Foraging & Feasting: A Field Guide and Wild Food Cookbook," New York: Botanical Arts Press, 2013. Seasonal Harvest Chart

(7)   Gladstar, Rosemary, "The Art and Science of Herbalism," Lesson 10 "Wild Herb Identification and Wild Food Cooking," Sage Mountain Press, 2014

(8)   History, "Creation of the Great Lakes: How the Earth Was Made," www.YouTube.com, January 23, 2021

(9)   Meuninck, Jim, "Edible Wild Plants & Useful Herbs" second ed., Connecticut: The Globe Pequot Press, 1999. p. vii

(10) Milwaukee Public Museum, "Great Lakes History: A General View," *www.mpm.edu/content/wirp/ICW-21#:~:tex*

(11) Michigan State University, "Indians in the Great Lakes Region," Indians in the Great Lakes region (msu.edu)

(12) My Canada, 5 Best Healthy Edible Seaweeds Grown in Canada – Find My Canada! October 29, 2021

(13) NASA Earth Observatory, "A Clear Spring View of the Great Lakes," A Clear Spring View of the Great Lakes (nasa.gov), March 25, 2019

(14) National Oceanic and Atmospheric Administration, Seen on: (*https://www.noaa.gov/education/resource-collections/freshwater/great-lakes-ecoregion*)

(15) Nyerges, Christopher, Guide to Edible Seaweeds, Mother Earth News, Guide to Edible Seaweed – Mother Earth News, April 11, 2014

(16) Osbourne, Lindi, Great Lakes Guide "Discover the Myths and Mysteries of the Great Lakes," April 12, 2019, Seen on: Discover the myths and mysteries of the Great Lakes | Great Lakes Guide

(17) Sardeshpande, Mallika, et al., "How People Foraging in Urban Greenspace Can Mobilize Social-Ecological Resilience During COVID 19 and Beyond" Frontiers, December 23, 2021

(18) Thayer, Sam, "The Forager's Harvest: A Guide to Identifying, Harvesting, and Preparing Edible Wild Plants," Wisconsin: Forager's Harvest Press, 2006

(19) Turtle, Alex, Diné (Navajo) and Southern Cheyenne, Chenoa Egawa, Lummi, and S'Klallam. "The Water Song" Seen on March 20, 2015: (366) The Water Song – Chenoa Egawa & Alex Turtle – YouTube

(20) Uva, Richard H., Joseph C. Neal, Joseph M DiTomaso, "Weeds of the Northeast," Ithaca, Cornell University Press, 1997. pp.375-383

6   Wild Food Harvesting, Preservation, and Storage Methods

6.1   The Seasonal Calendar

Your preservation methods depend on your penchant for different foods, your harvesting experience, and the volume of wild food harvested. Discovering a plant, gathering it, and consuming it is a memorable experience. However, you want good memories instead of unpleasant ones. Simple guidelines will help you experience foraging all year. First, it is essential to know what types of plants to harvest from season to season. Check the short seasonal harvesting list below and then refer to the seasonal calendar for month by month guidance.   .

Early Spring – tubers, roots, flowers, and perennial greens
Mid-spring – tubers, roots, seaweeds, flowers, and perennial greens
Late Spring to Early Summer – shoots, stalks, seaweeds, and greens of all types
Late summer – fruits, seeds, seaweeds, and nuts
Early fall – nuts, fruits, seeds, tubers, seaweeds, and roots
Late fall – tubers, roots, nuts, seaweeds, and seeds
Winter – tubers, roots, nuts, seaweeds, and seeds

After looking at the chart and understanding what you can harvest week by week, turn your attention to *how to harvest*. Follow the fundamental rule of gently harvesting a plant with conservation in mind. Be careful when you cut a plant or walk near it. Proceed patiently without being overly ambitious. Allow plenty of time for your harvesting and preparation process. Nothing is more disappointing than gathering a precious herb and letting it waste.

When you harvest something, wash it before consumption. Pick the cleaner plants if you choose between harvesting a dirty plant or a more pristine patch. Washing a lot of dirt from a plant is a very lengthy process. Make sure to get all of the earth out of the grooves in the plant or root. Sometimes foragers are disappointed when their foraging hobby takes too much time. Digging, picking, washing, drying, and peeling is a long process. Starting small and harvesting less is wise in the beginning.

Seasonal calendar for month by month guidance on when to collect different plants.

Plant	Parts used	Spring			Summer			Fall			Winter		
		Early	Middle	Late	Early	Middle	Late	Early	Middle	Late	Early	Middle	Late
Asparagus (Wild)	stalk		■	■									
Asparagus officinalis													
Chickweed	leaves, stems, and flowers	■				■							
Stellaria Media													
Dandelion	root, leaf, or flower					■							
Taraxacum officinale													
Garlic Mustard	aerial parts	■			■								
Alliaria petiolata													
Mint	aerial parts						■	■					
Mentha piperita													
Oyster Mushrooms	fungus head and stem								■				
Pleurotus ostreatus													
Nettle	leaves						■						
Urtica dioica													
Plantain	leaves or aerial parts												
Plantago Major													
Sheep Sorrel	leaves, stems, and roots						■						
Rumex acetosella													

Plant	Parts used	Spring			Summer			Fall			Winter		
		Early	Middle	Late	Early	Middle	Late	Early	Middle	Late	Early	Middle	Late
Wild Garlic	bulb, flowers, stems	▓		▓									
Allium Sativum													
Spice Bush	berries, leaves, bark, stems	▓	▓						▓				
Lindera Benzoin													
Trout Lily	leaves	▓											
Erythronium Americanum													
Violets	leaves and flowers	▓											
Viola spp.													
Black-Eyed Susan	seeds, flowers				▓	▓	▓	▓					
Asteraceae													
Blessed Thistle	leaves and early-blooming flower				▓	▓	▓	▓	▓				
Cnicus benedictus													
Boneset	dried aerial parts				▓		▓	▓					
Eupatorium Perfoliatum													
Forsythia	flowers, fruit, and bark		▓	▓	▓	▓	▓	▓	▓	▓			
Forsythia suspensa													

Plant	Parts used	Spring			Summer			Fall			Winter		
		Early	Middle	Late	Early	Middle	Late	Early	Middle	Late	Early	Middle	Late
Goldenrod	aerial parts				■	■	■	■	■				
Solidago													
Green Brier (Sarsaparilla)	leaves, roots			■	■	■	■	■	■	■			
Smilax Rotundifolia													
Prairie Moon	root					■							
Astragalus Canadensis													
Prairie Rose	flower			■	■	■	■						
Rosa arkansana	fruit/rosehip				■	■	■	■					
Raspberries (Wild)	berries				■	■	■						
Rubus idaeus	leaves, roots				■	■	■	■					
Milkweed	flowers				■								
Asclepias speciosa													
Meadowsweet	aerial parts				■	■	■						
Filipendula ulmaria													
Mugwort	leaves					■	■	■					
Artemisia Vulgaris													
Mullein	leaf			■	■	■	■						
Verbascum thapsus	flower				■	■							

Plant	Parts used	Spring Early	Middle	Late	Summer Early	Middle	Late	Fall Early	Middle	Late	Winter Early	Middle	Late
Oat seed/Oatstraw	fresh, young oat seeds					▪	▪						
Avena Sativa													
Purple Dead Nettle	leaves, stems, and flowers		▪	▪	▪	▪							
Lamium purpureum													
Purslane	leaves, stems, flowers						▪	▪					
Portulaca oleracea													
Serviceberry	berries, bark				▪		▪						
Amelanchier spp.													
Thimbleberry	berries				▪								
Rubus parviflorus													
Yarrow	aerial parts		▪	▪	▪	▪	▪						
Achillea millefolium													
Autumn Olive	flowers, olives, seeds						▪	▪					
Elaeagnus umbellata													
Butternut	nut							▪	▪				
Juglans cinera													
Burdock (Great)	root	▪	▪	▪	▪	▪	▪	▪	▪	▪			
Article minus													
Cattail	shoots	▪											

Plant	Parts used	Spring			Summer			Fall			Winter		
		Early	Middle	Late	Early	Middle	Late	Early	Middle	Late	Early	Middle	Late
Typha Latifolia	roots head			X	X	X	X						
Ground Nuts	seed, tuber			X	X	X	X	X	X	X			
Apios americana													
Maple	leaves		X					X					
Acer	sap	X											
Staghorn Sumac	berries from the conical head							X			X		
Rhus spp.													
Wild Mallow	leaves			X	X	X	X		X				
Malva neglecta	flowers			X				X					
Birch Bark	leaves, buds	X	X	X	X								
Betula pubescens	bark	X	X	X	X	X	X	X	X	X	X	X	X
Pine	needles												
Pinus Sylvestris	buds												
Oak	leaves, bark	X	X	X	X	X	X	X	X	X	bark only	bark only	bark only
Quercus, spp., Faceae	acorns												
White Willow	bark, pith	X	X	X	X	X	X	X	X	X	X	X	X
Salix alba													

6.2 Sustainable Practices for Harvesting Plants

Many people disregard the weeds in their backyard as useless. Yet if you look more closely, those weeds provide precious foraging opportunities. Just start in your backyard by picking dandelion or nettle leaves. Perhaps you'll find violets growing on your lawn. I picked Garlic Mustard just the other day and ate it for lunch. It saved me a trip to the grocery store. Foraging helps us understand how the farmer lives, how the gardener spends his time, or how long it takes to catch a fish. Everything we eat requires extensive preparation. Foraging helps us become grateful for all of these efforts.

These tips will help you forage effectively while preserving the plants' species and ensuring their reproduction. Below, you will find pictures that clarify the terms in the text.

1. We have already discussed that one should leave 30% of the plant alone. Although it is tempting to over-pick flowers, leave a third of them behind to go to seed.

2. Again, it is worth reminding ourselves not to harvest endangered species such as Wild Ginseng, a federally protected plant. To know which plants are at risk, consider the list of endangered plants and the species-at-risk assessment tool of the North American organization, *United Plant Savers. The direct link to the list and assessment tool are: https://unitedplantsavers.org/species-at-risk-list/ and https://unitedplantsavers.org/species-at-risk-assessment-tool/.*

3. If a plant is genuinely invasive and chokes out other valuable varieties of plant life, then it is OK to remove the plant from its roots. Garlic Mustard is a good example. Generally, your local Forestry Department will be able to tell you which local species are invasive.

4. Ensure that you leave enough seeds to grow new plants if you harvest an annual plant.

5. Leaving partial roots or only taking a portion of a root patch ensures that the plant will regenerate.

6. Reduce plants if they look too crowded and are not thriving.

7. Harvest leaves and fragile stems by clipping them. Otherwise, you might pull on the plant too hard and render it useless.

8. If you grow plants yourself, like nettle, mint, or lemon balm, harvest them at their nodes. They will reproduce much more quickly this way.

9. Cut shoots a couple of inches above the ground so that the lower portion can regenerate.

10. Leave as many seeds behind as possible from any plant so they can resow themselves.

11. Fruits have various reproduction methods. They reproduce themselves via the seed, the stem, and the root. It is an excellent practice to leave some fruit on the plant for wildlife and reproduction.

12. Plants like mint, nettle, and groundnuts have runners sprawl underneath the ground. Make sure that you don't pull up too many of the running roots.

6.3 Harvesting and Preparing Guidelines for Different Plant Parts

6.3.1 Greens

Greens are the leafy and edible part of a plant. Herbalists and holistic practitioners often point out that although we certainly need the high fiber, protein, and minerals that leafy greens provide, we avoid consuming them due to their bitterness. Yet, greens fortify our blood and assist liver function. Learning to gather greens is a precious contribution to our health. Before you avoid their bitter taste, ask yourself what function bitterness serves.

Consequently, you may tolerate greens instead of avoiding the taste when you ask yourself this question. Try to pick the younger and more tender leaves. If leaves are too rigid, you won't want to chew them, and they may taste too bitter. Light green growth at the end of a stem, stalk, or branch generally tastes better. If you like, use a sauce with spices over your greens or put a dressing on your raw greens after cooking. Materia Medica contains recipes for tasty wild greens combinations you will love.

Spring and early summer are the ideal time to harvest greens. According to ancient medicinal calendars, our liver and gallbladder automatically detoxify during the spring season. Greens assist the detoxification process. Each season, a different organ system naturally detoxifies itself. It is a complex process, fascinating, yet beyond the scope of this book. For now, try to develop at least a habit of harvesting spring 'cleansing' greens to assist your livers' detoxification process. Try to pick the younger spring green leaves before they become older and harder to chew.

You can cook most of the greens listed in this book. I usually do not cook sheep sorrel. It is delicate and best eaten raw as a salad green. A smaller amount is better if you eat raw wild greens due to the bitter taste. Remember that wild greens contain more highly concentrated nutrients than most lettuce that you purchase in the supermarket. The heartier greens like nettle and dandelion are often best as a salad, mixed with something sweeter like grated carrots or cabbage. You can boil greens, add them to a simple broth or steam them. Sauteeing is always an option.

6.3.2   Shoots

Shoots contain a plant's energy waiting to grow into a stem. A stem is the delivery system of the plant. Therefore, shoots are the concentrated power of a plant's delivery system. Shoots in this book include asparagus or cattail shoots. Search for shoots with a substantial diameter, without too many leaves that are also tender, and bend easily. The portion of a shoot that bends is the softest and most edible. Bend, pinch, and cut the shoot just above the rigid part. You will have to eat your shoots within three to four days. They are tasty, boiled or steamed, and cooked thoroughly in soups. You can eat raw shoots or put them in salads. When you cook them, bear in mind that it is a short process. A few minutes or less is acceptable. Picking shoots is also an option well worth exploring.

6.3.3   Roots and Tubers

Underground harvesting will take place from the fall until early spring when the upper portion of the plant is dormant. Many veteran foragers and herbalists refer to this time as root season. Being able to dig for roots and tubers means that you can complete your foraging feast with more concentrated calories and protein. If you ever truly needed to survive on foraged food, roots and tubers would become crucial for consumption. Though the digging process is sometimes arduous for beginners, it yields more bulk and substance faster than picking greens. Underground harvesting is immensely satisfying.

There are digging sticks that you can make yourself. Shorter-handled digging tools are easier to maneuver for extracting shorter roots. Sometimes, if you are unprepared, you may find a stick in the wild and dig with it.

Burdock or dandelion have longer roots, often grow in rocky soil, and might require a shovel. You do not have to wash the roots or tubers you dig up right away. You can store them if they have a coating of dirt. Ensure your storage area for underground foods is dark and dry, or your products will gather mold. However, it would be best if you washed them thoroughly before consumption. Be sure to clean all the cracks and crevices where dirt can hide. A vegetable scrub brush can help.

Baking, boiling, slicing/roasting, or frying roots and tubers are preparation options.

Groundnuts are tubers with a high starch content and a sprawling root
system that links one tuber to another.

6.3.4   Berries

When you pick berries, it is crucial to have the proper container to put
them in. Berries are delicate. If you pile them on top of one another, it
will crush them. The secret to berry harvesting is to put them in a flat
container so that the berries do not destroy one another. When you
pick the berries, empty them into a larger flat container kept on the
ground to preserve their shape. Wild strawberries, raspberries, blackberries, autumn olives, blueberries, serviceberries, and especially thimbleberries need careful handling. Otherwise, they will become mushy.

Hot weather spoils your berries within a few hours of picking them.
So it is best to designate a particular day to pick berries so that you can
focus on getting home relatively soon to prepare them. You can only
keep wild berries in the refrigerator for a day or two before they wither
away. Freezing berries in small bags or containers are the fastest way to
preserve them. Also, it makes them available for different preparations
later.

You can make jams, jellies, syrups, fruit leathers, juices, baked goods, sauces, and many other things with berries. It is easiest, of course, to eat them directly. Just make sure they are clean from dirt and animal contamination so you don't catch an illness.

6.3.5 Nuts

Nutmeat is an essential foraging category. Nuts have been a traditional staple food for foraging populations for centuries. Along with berries, they provide critical nourishment. One can find nuts easily, such as acorns and butternuts listed in the Materia Medica of this book. Nuts provide oils, starches, and protein, as well as carbohydrates. For their size, they offer a potent and efficient source of nutrition. In an actual survival situation, nuts would be critical for sustenance. An added benefit is that they store very well. In a tightly capped, dry container, nuts will last for a year. You may also freeze them.

Ideally, you will often find nuts right on the ground where they have fallen. Other times you might shake a tree with nuts so that the ripe ones fall close to you. You can knock nuts down from a tree with a long stick also. The trick is to distinguish the good nuts from the rotten ones. Sometimes nuts have worms. However, there are signs that a nut has worms, such as holes or rotten parts on the outer surface. Don't gather or open nuts like these, or you may be disappointed.

Nutcrackers work for smaller nuts, but a hammer used on a piece of wood or stone is often best. Always wear work gloves, so you do not hit your finger directly with a hammer. Large nuts with hard shells require a pretty forceful hit. Once you crack the nut, use a nut pick to gouge the inside and get all the meat. Sometimes on larger pieces, you will be able to use your fingers. If you cannot extract a portion of a nut from a shell, it is OK. Leave those pieces outside for the critters to enjoy.

With what you harvest, you can make nut flours, trail mixes, baked goods, sauces, different types of pesto, or even nut butter.

Worms in nut shell (right)

6.3.6　Seaweed

Various cultures worldwide have used varieties of seaweed for hundreds of years. The nutritional value of edible seaweeds is very high because they contain proteins, vitamins, minerals, and dietary fiber. Harvesting them is well worth it if you and your family can develop a taste for this wonder food. Only basic guidelines are included in this book. When you plan to forage water plants, *you must check with a local forager to understand what to harvest from area to area.*

1.　Check the weather and barometric pressure readings in the area to ensure that you will not harvest in any extreme or inclement condition. Wait for the best possible weather, and take what is closer to the shore.

2.　Avoid industrial areas or near farmland with potent pesticides that run into the water.

3.　Watch out for rocks while you are harvesting to not trip over them.

4.　The closer the seaweed gets to the shore, the more of an opportunity the insects have to feast on it. Avoid them and look for fresh pieces.

5. When seaweed is anchored to a rock, do not just yank on it. You might disturb other sea creatures living on the rock, and your harvest might contain debris. If you can collect it from flowing freshwater, for instance in the case of varieties of kombu, it will taste better and is less likely to be contaminated.

6. Just snip a few and leave the rest of the plant alone to reproduce. Trim the unwanted ends before you take them home to lighten your load.

7. Rinse the leaves well in freshwater.

8. Then hang it dry with a towel underneath. Some people use a plastic hanger. Others attach it to a rack with clothespins. Some dry it on a pasta rack or a laundry line.

9. Once it is dry, place it in a tightly sealed bag or container. You can store it in a cool dark place for up to a year. Indeed, seaweeds are one of the most accessible forms of plant life to harvest and store.

Drying seaweeds

6.4   Preserving and Storing your Harvest

There are substantial benefits to learning preservation and storage methods for your wild harvest. For instance, you can save time shopping and money. There is a plus when you know where your food comes from and the natural substances. Gathering food with your loved ones and consuming it throughout the year due to preservation brings a sense of security and resourcefulness. For those in colder climates, preservation and storage mean shopping less during bad or cold weather periods. Last but not least, you might be able to use some of the things you preserve as gifts. So while the preservation process takes time, it adds time and reduces stress in some ways.

However, if you would rather buy your goods from the grocery store or even a farm stand or farmer's market, that is fine. The following preservation methods progress from easiest to hardest.

6.4.1   Freezing

Freezing is the most common and user-friendly way to store what you harvest. This method captures food value while it is fresh and preserves it. Most importantly, it saves time. Fancy equipment is not required. You need containers or bags that seal correctly. Use frozen goods within a year, or they will get freezer burn and become inedible. Before freezing, you can blanch your vegetables, especially greens. The process maintains the plant's enzymes and particular plant cells. Hopefully, you have enough freezer space for long-term storage. If not, other options may be more helpful.

6.4.2   Drying

Dehydration, next to freezing, is also a user-friendly preparation and storage option. When something contains almost no moisture, you can keep it in many cases for months to even years. Drying does not take up space in your freezer. You can dry almost anything you forage, including greens, berries, seeds, grains, nuts, tubers or roots, and sea vegetables. Drying thick succulent leaves is not recommended. They do not dry well. Shoots also contain too much water and become mushy when they are dehydrated. You'll want to avoid drying them.

Greens are best dried when you bind the stems together and dry them upside down. Choose a corner to hang them that is clean and not too bright. The leaves maintain their color and integrity and do not become brown. On the other hand, if you dried them in the sunlight, they would become discolored and desiccated. Once they are dried, you can crush them and put them in soups, stir fry, casseroles, or pasta. Dehydrated greens will work in any recipe that calls for greens.

Roots and tubers dry very well. Slice them thinly and place them on a baking tray. Some People create or purchase a rack for baking trays if they become more serious about foraging and dehydrating more than a couple of things. You can line the baking tray with an old clean paper bag or parchment paper to absorb the moisture and help your wild goods dry more effectively. If the trays are stacked, they will not take up space. However, in a warmer area of your home, you can criss-cross the trays on a flat surface if you dry a few things. That does not take up so much space. Or, you can dry them in an oven on very low heat, 115 degrees Fahrenheit, for six to eight hours. There are also commercial electric drier available like the dehydrator in the picture below.

Rose hips are drying in the oven. Dried rose hips are an important source of vitamin C and antioxidants.

Electric food dehydrator. In the picture mushrooms are dried but the drier can be used on a variety of herbs, fruits and vegetables.

6.4.3 Cold Storage/Root Cellar

The very best method of cold storage is to leave the roots you find where you are until just before they become impossible to dig up from the frozen earth. Utilize the most natural method of storage first. Dig up your roots and tubers before the ground becomes hard, but make sure that you do not bruise them or damage the skin. When your underground harvest is damaged, the roots and tubers will not last in cold storage. There is an added benefit to leaving roots in the ground. It gives you a chance to store and utilize your fall harvest first. At the same time, other roots and tubers for winter consumption remain safely stored in a natural environment.

Cold storage has distinct benefits. First and foremost, the food stays fresh in its natural state. Also, it hardly takes any preparation efforts. It is OK if you do not have a root cellar or base. You can keep a bucket with your harvest outside and cover it with leaves or wood shavings. When it gets too cold, and the frost deepens, bring the bucket in and put it in a cardboard box. Try to cover it with wood shavings and place it in the coldest part of your house. Ensure that the box remains dry while in storage; otherwise, your harvest will mold. This simple method keeps your harvest fresh for months.

Additionally, if you have a little extra space in your refrigerator, you can wrap your harvest in a cloth and keep it in the corner of the fridge. You cannot store leaves and stalks or fruit this way. Whatever you store must be completely intact. Cranberries and apples have thicker skin and do very well in long-term cold storage; however, they are the exceptions to the rule. Nuts, roots, and tubers are ideal for cold storage.

Seaweed Preparation

Edible seaweed is often called the secret superfood of preppers. If you can utilize even a small amount of seaweed, you will be well nourished. Generally, the most commonly harvested saltwater seaweeds include dulse, laver, sea lettuce, kelp, and Irish moss.

You can generally dry and grind most seaweeds into powder and then use them even if they are thick and chewy. Over time you will learn the most realistic seaweeds to prepare. However, stick with a couple of simple choices.

One can consume seaweeds in the following ways:

1. eaten raw (only for absolute seaweed connoisseurs);

2. dried, crushed, and put into soups, stews, or stir fry;

3. dried, powdered, and made into salty seasonings – sometimes even a salt substitute;

4. as a thickening agent in jellies, candies, puddings, ice cream, or gravy;

5. to flavor fish or clams;

6. dried in strips and eaten just like someone would chew on beef jerky;

7. it is boiled into a seaweed broth or placed in a pot with other vegetables to make a delicious soup.

Seaweeds make suitable thickeners because of their gummy quality. If you would like to store seaweed, cook it for thirty minutes. Blend it in a blender and strain it through a mesh wire strainer or a muslin cloth to separate the solids. Make a label, and then put it in the fridge. It has multiple uses as plant food or pet food. In addition, once prepared, it is easy to use as a soup base or thickener for homemade ice cream or pudding.

6.5   Water Bath Canning

Canning is the most lengthy process of all the storage methods. However, it is worth considering if you plan to take foraging seriously. Canning sterilizes your food so that it will not spoil. Heat sterilizes both the food and the storage container. You can store canned foods for a year in a cool place. If you process your jam in a hot water bath, it will last two years. Always refer back to a reliable canning guide for safety if you are uncertain about something or talk to someone who has had many years of canning experience.

When the jar is filled and then heated, it will create steam. The steam expands and pushes the air from the pot. However, as the air cools, it has the opposite effect. It condenses the jar contents and creates a vacuum seal on the jar. Inappropriate amounts of sugar and acid can cause problems in the canning process. It is always best to follow time-tested recipes. You can substitute foraged ingredients for common ingredients.

There are two primary canning methods:

The first is water bath canning. This method has a lower temperature and is perfect for foods with high acid content (e.g., fruits, tomatoes, pickles, chutneys, or other fillings and condiments).

The second method is pressure canning. Vegetables, soups, etc., fall into this category. The USDA does not recommend using a pressure cooker for canning. There are too many problems with the method, so it is not recommended here.

Essential tools for canning include:

1. A large pot or a proper water bath canner;
2. clean and dry your jars with sealing lids, like Ball Jars or Mason Jars.
3. When your jars are too hot to lift, you will need a pair of tongs with rubber tips to grasp and lift the pot from the hot water so you can fill it.
4. Keep a ladle near the process to pour your food into the jars.
5. When you fill the jar, a wide-mouthed funnel helps to keep food from running over the jar's edges.

Remember that trusted jar brands are the most reliable. Avoid used jars that may have residue underneath the cover that you cannot see. Anything that is not sterile will create a problem later.

6.5.1   Water Bath Canning – Basic Steps

1. Wash your jars in hot soapy water, and then rinse them in hot water.

2. Place your jars in a water bath canner or a clean, deep pot. Use hot tap water to cover your jars completely with an inch of water over the top.

3. Simmer the jars over medium heat for ten minutes.

4. Put your lids into a clean bowl while the jars are still simmering in hot water.

5. Using your ladle, take some hot water out of the pot and pour it into the bowl to cover the lids.

6. Now you are ready to use your sterilized jars and your lids.

7. Place a couple of kitchen towels next to one another on a flat surface near your pot and bowl.

8. Using your tongs, take the jars from the pot, empty the water, and put the jar on your cloth. It will dry quickly.

9. Repeat this process with your lids and let them steam dry on the towel.

10. Pour food into the jar using a ladle and funnel.

11. Leave a ¼ inch space between the food and the jar's top edge.

12. Poke out any bubbles with a chopstick, so they burst.

13. Wipe the rims of your jars until they are clean.

14. Screw the lids on, making sure to do it efficiently while the jars and the food are still hot.

15. After the jars cool, test the effectiveness of the seal by pressing the center of the jar lid. If the top pops or moves up and down, the jar is not sealed correctly.

16. If your jar does not seal, make sure and use the contents within three days. Otherwise, you have to process the contents all over again – sorry – that part can be rather disappointing. Sterilization and canning of the food a second time must occur within 24 hours.

17. Otherwise, if you are satisfied the jars are sealed, store them in a cool dark place for up to a year.

Funnel used to fill the food into jars.

6.5.2 How Can You Tell If Canned Goods Have Spoiled?

Consider that spoiled food causes food poisoning more often than becoming poisoned by eating the wrong plant. Take your canning process seriously to prevent spoilage and hence food poisoning.

Here are red flags one must detect:

1. a broken seal or bulging lid;

2. rust or corrosion on the lid;

3. bubbles in the food upon opening the can;

4. any food with a haze or cloud over it or any food that looks the slightest bit moldy;

5. a funny or displeasing odor when you open the container.

It is essential to throw away spoiled canned goods as soon as you find them. You may be tempted to rescue your preparations. However, if you do, you may have to go back and use the food poisoning section of this book. Please take the signs of spoilage seriously to enjoy what you prepare safely. Now speaking of enjoyment, let's turn to ways to create a day off or even a vacation to connect deeper with the natural world.

7   Foraging Locations and Learning Opportunities

The sustainability of ecosystems is critical. Although we discussed that foraging laws prohibited indigenous populations from pursuing their way of life at the beginning of the book, there is another aspect to foraging legally. Currently, some are tempted to over harvest and sell what they procure. Others may want to stockpile wild edibles without thinking about depleting plants or even herbs on the verge of extinction. Thus, laws are created to protect plants. One must check the local regulations that apply to the area they wish to forage through Forestry Departments or Parks and Recreation Departments in North America. This certainly includes foraging in Canada.

Responsible foraging practices go along with sustainable agricultural practices. Sustainable farming practices do not just apply to farmers. They apply to all of us. This book cannot cover sustainable agricultural practices like growing your edibles or medicinal plants. However, it does provide some references to learn more about growing your food. Part of the reason for listing opportunities that indigenous cultural organizations provide is to tap into their knowledge and learn from other cultures. Various foraging courses can teach you ways to fit foraging or sustainable agricultural practices into your own life.

Over 120 Native American tribes have occupied the Great Lakes region during several thousand years. There is a detailed list of historic tribes and modern tribes in the Great Lakes Region. It encompasses Illinois, Michigan, Wisconsin, Ohio, and Indiana. The U.S. National Archives hold this comprehensive research guide for historic and modern indigenous communities in these states. The reference below is provided so that, if desired, you can learn about where current tribes are located.

Great Lakes Native Communities Research Guide (archives.gov) (www.archives.gov/files/education/native-communities/great-lakes-nativecommunities-guide.pdf)

7.1   Native American Organizations, Maps & References

Some states have a more significant indigenous population than others. Also, the states that contain the most resources currently are the ones where dedicated activists have ensured that the integrity of land usage and the traditional indigenous way of life is restored. It is an ongoing process involving the tireless efforts of many activists from different disciplines. States such as Michigan and the province of Ontario in Canada have a very active foraging population and a more visible indigenous community than some of the other states such as Ohio and Indiana. In 2016 there were approximately 374, 395 members of the aboriginal community in Ontario.

Currently, there are no Indian reservations in Ohio, for instance. Similarly, two tribes have reservation land in Indiana, the Potawatomi and the Miami. There are approximately 25,000 members of Native American tribes presently living in Indiana.

7.1.1   Jijak Foundation

The Jijak Foundation is a nonprofit organization that strives "to preserve, perpetuate, and share the rich history, culture, arts, and living traditions of the Gun Lake Band of Pottawatomi Indians as a valuable investment to strengthen their tribal community." The Foundation provides Potawatomi and Ojibwe tribes chances to save and restore their at-risk crops. They have a seed library, and local tribal leaders create traditional community meals from their harvest to spread awareness. Connect with this fantastic resource using these links.

1. Read the following article; Sanders, Corinne, **'Native American Communities Are Saving Rare Plants From Edge Of Extinction. – InspireMore'**, **August 20, 2020.**

2. Connect with foraging groups on Facebook. One reference is **'(20+) Jijak Foundation | Facebook'**.

3. Read their website and contact them. **Camp Jijak | Gun Lake Tribe (gunlaketribe-nsn.gov)**

7.1.2   Red Lake Ojibwe Nation

Red Lake Nation is located at 15484 Migizi Drive, Red Lake, MN 56671. In Minnesota, the Red Lake Nation collaborates with other organizations to offer sustainable agriculture and wild harvesting courses. You can connect with their website: **Red Lake Nation – Home of the Red Lake Band of Chippewa Indians' (https://www.redlakenation. org/).** Red Lake is structured to serve the indigenous community and provides outreach opportunities to raise awareness.

7.1.3   White Earth Nation

The White Earth Nation has an active wild harvesting and agricultural practices awareness and education program. The White Earth Reservation contains 829,440 acres and is located in northwestern Minnesota. It encompasses all of Mahnomen County and portions of Becker and Clearwater Counties. The reservation is located 68 miles east of Fargo and 225 miles northwest of Minneapolis/St. Paul. The Tribal headquarters is located in White Earth, Minnesota. In 1981, White Earth Band of Chippewa v. Alexander reaffirmed tribal treaty rights for tribal members on the reservation to hunt, fish, and gather wild rice free of state regulations on all land within the White Earth Reservation. Please see their homepage, **https://whiteearth.com/.**

In June, the White Earth Reservation offers a Food Summit. Please refer to this article, **'Mary Pember: Foraging for food on White Earth Reservation (indianz.com)'.**

Otherwise, see the Minnesota Indian Affairs Council Website for additional information on White Earth Nation, **'MN Indian Affairs Council: Gaa-waabaabiganikaag / White Earth Nation' (https:// mn.gov/indianaffairs/whiteearth-iac.html).**

7.1.4   IAC Intertribal Agriculture Council

The IAC has, over the last three decades, become recognized as the most respected voice within the Indian community and government circles on agricultural policies and programs in North America. Please see the following link, **'Intertribal Agriculture Council EVENTS | IAC' (indianag.org).**

The Intertribal Agriculture Council offers a yearly Food Sovereignty Symposium and Festival. Part of their focus is on agricultural conservation and land stewardship. Please see the following link, **'InterTribal Agriculture Council Food Summit 2021 ANNUAL CONFERENCE | IAC (indianag.org)'.**

Ontario has developed some very unique resources for indigenous cultural awareness. It has a substantial population of Native Americans. To date, one hundred and twenty-three First Nations in Ontario exist. They have jurisdiction over two hundred and seven reserves. By 2019 more than 218, 451 Indians registered as residents in Ontario. Forty-four percent of that population live in reservations. The main reservations are headed by Anishinaabe, Cree, Oji-Cree, Haudenosaunee, Delaware, and Algonquin peoples. Other First Nations in Ontario are also established, yet due to various factors, they don't have reservation land.

The First Nations Confederacy of Cultural Education Centres directs multiple cultural centers throughout Ontario. Its mission is quite comprehensive as it provides education and training in primary and secondary schools, teaching materials, summer camps, traditional sweat lodges, and ceremonies. In general, it strives to preserve the teachings of Native American elders through community outreach. It is well worth reading their website, and just a glance at it is an educational opportunity in and of itself. Please see their website **FNCCEC – www. fnccec.ca** for education-related programs, including curriculum development for Band and provincial schools, teacher training, language classes, language acquisition, resource support to schools, presentations, workshops relating to the preservation of culture and language, and life skills development.

7.2 Foraging Resources Surrounding the Great Lakes

Camping excursions are a way to practice your plant identification skills and perhaps find a patch of available land to practice harvesting. Once more, rules apply. For instance, harvesting wild Ginseng is federally banned on public grounds because it is an endangered plant. Foraging ramps or wild onions are popular, even trendy. Yet, some rules regulate their procurement in various areas due to overharvesting. Having said that, once you search, you will find a place to begin. This book helps point you in the right direction.

Start by understanding the available camping opportunities. The following article is an excellent overview of lesser-known camping areas in each Great Lakes state.

Fabulous Hidden Gems for Great Lakes Camping [2022 Edition] (backroadramblers.com)

An outstanding resource for foragers and nature lovers of all types is Camp Jijak, owned and operated by the Jijak Foundation.

Camp Jijak combines fun, a family adventure, and a way to learn more about foraging and indigenous traditions. Hopkins, Michigan, offers camping, trails, a tribal garden, and a seasonal calendar of traditional ceremonies and workshops. It features a tribal garden in Hopkins from April through October on 126th Ave. From October through November, you can learn about wild rice processing. Rice harvesting is only one of the many courses offered throughout the year. Otherwise, there is a lengthy network of trails and a lake where you can swim, and if you time your visit just right, you can attend a traditional indigenous ceremony like the Sweetgrass Moon Pow Wow in mid-July. Please see the following link, **Camp Jijak | Gun Lake Tribe (gunlaketribe-nsn.gov)**

The following resource is nationwide. It contains valuable references that will help you connect with an experienced forager or foraging course in your area. It has many resources from the states surrounding the Great Lakes. Please see this link, **Forager's Harvest – List of Foraging Classes and Resources (foragersharvest.com).**

The Intertribal Food Summit

A collaboration including the Jijak Foundation, The University of Wisconsin, College of Menominee Nation, Red Lake Nation, and the Sustainable Development Institute provides fantastic opportunities to learn about tribal agriculture in Michigan, Minnesota, and Wisconsin. They host an annual Intertribal Food Summit every year that teaches sustainable foraging and farming practices in addition to wild harvest cooking skills. They also host field days and classes and a webinar series. Speakers and teachers have farming expertise and fantastic foraging knowledge in different areas, yet all come from tribal communities. Please see **2021 Great Lakes Workshops | Great Lakes Region IAC Website (iacgreatlakes.com).**

7.3   Laws and Regulations about Foraging in U.S. Great Lakes States and Canada Ontario Province

7.3.1   Ontario

In Ontario, Foraging is illegal in public parks. However, on the whole, Ontario is a forager-friendly paradise. There are many foraging classes, conferences, and treks in this area. However, before exploring your options, please see the following article about where foraging is illegal— the **effects of foraging at Ontario Parks (https://www.ontarioparks. com/).** Otherwise, you might enjoy a foraging class through one of these venues listed below.

Foraging Tours and Classes in Ontario – Eat The Planet (https:// eattheplanet.org/)

Pucks Plenty features guided foraging treks. An expert will lead participants down incredible woodland trails all over Southern Ontario. This organization aims to educate trekkers to forage responsibly and effectively. They teach participants about both wild edibles and wild mushrooms.

Ontario Foraging – Foraging, Wild edibles, Wild Mushrooms, Stratford restaurants, oyster mushrooms, morels (pucksplenty. com)

7.3.2 Michigan

Camp Jijak – Gun Lake Tribe

Camp Jijak is a beautiful resource for foragers of all ages. It is mentioned in previous sections of this book as a Native American learning center and foraging resource. It combines fun with family adventure and a way to learn more about foraging and indigenous traditions. In Hopkins, Michigan, Camp Jijak offers camping, trails, a tribal garden, and a seasonal calendar of traditional ceremonies and workshops. You could call it a one-stop-shop, which is why it is mentioned in more than one place.

From April through October, it features a tribal garden on 126th Ave. From October through November, you can learn about wild rice processing. Otherwise, there is a lengthy network of trails and a lake where you can swim, and if you time your visit just right, you can attend a traditional indigenous ceremony like the Sweetgrass Moon Pow Wow in mid-July. Please see the following link, **Camp Jijak | Gun Lake Tribe (gunlaketribe-nsn.gov).**

The following article is an excellent overview of lesser-known camping areas in each Great Lakes state. Please see **Fabulous Hidden Gems for Great Lakes Camping [2022 Edition] (backroadramblers.com).**

Michigan State University Foragers Connection is one way to find knowledgeable foragers and classes. They have a yearly schedule. Please see **Events (msu.edu).**

Michigan State University Extension lists foraging courses regularly. Some of them are perfect for beginners. Please see **foraging for free food – MSU Extension, https://www.canr.msu.edu/news/foraging_ for_free_food.**

7.3.3   Minnesota

There are many foraging options in Minnesota. Organized foraging events include the '**North House Folk School in Grand Marais'**, which teaches a single-day course in the spring.

The Ely Folk School' offers foraging and wild rice harvest courses. '**The Minnesota 'Department of Natural Resources'** provides a "Becoming An Outdoors Woman" program.

Please see the following link for even more exciting possibilities, '**Explore Minnesota's Great Outdoors by Foraging | Explore Minnesota'** (**https://www.exploreminnesota.com/article/explore-minnesotas-great-outdoors-foraging**).

Since wild mushroom harvesting is reaching peak popularity, it may be worth taking a particular private course that will ensure a great harvest and your safety. The primary facilitators at this site collaborate with the Department of Natural Resources to offer an Outdoors Skills Academy plus courses in mushroom identification. Please see **Great Lakes Treats (https://greatlakestreats.com/).**

7.3.4   Wisconsin

Sam Thayer, a master forager, offers courses in Wisconsin. This book acknowledges his vast expertise. Please see this link, **Classes – Forager's Harvest (foragersharvest.com).**

The Dane County Parks System allows public foraging. It contains a network of trails and educational opportunities. Specific regulations and sustainable harvesting practices apply. Please see **Foraging | Dane County Parks (countyofdane.com).**

7.3.5   Ohio

Foraging for mushrooms in most U.S. States Parks is illegal. However, Ohio is a bit different. In Ohio, one needs a permit to forage. Certain cities may allow foraging in public parks, but you have to call ahead to get clearance. Ohio is known as mushroom foraging territory. Mid-April through May is the perfect time to search for fungi. You can connect with the Ohio State Park of your choice to see if they allow mushroom hunting. If you collect plants on state parkland, you must stay on the trail. Foraging off the trails is not permitted. Check for special rules that may apply to particular state park areas.

Since 1973 Ohio has had a Mushroom Society. Taking advantage of their courses or even becoming a long-term affiliate will give you a way to increase your knowledge. Beginning foraging classes are offered. Professional mycologists (those who study fungi) and mycophagists (mushroom eaters) provide courses for more advanced foragers. Anyone is welcome to participate. Follow this link to connect, **'Ohio Mushroom Society' (https://ohiomushroomsociety.wordpress.com/).**

If you plan to camp and forage, call the state park in your vacation destination to find out the specific foraging rules. The following website offers information on foraging and contains a comprehensive list of state park facilities and camping options. Is **'it legal to forage in Ohio state parks? – SidmartinBio' (https://www.sidmartinbio.org/ is-it-legal-to-forage-in-ohio-state-parks/).**

7.3.6   Indiana

Indiana has a fair number of resources for the forager. Please see the following state park website to connect with state parks in Indiana. Inquire about what foraging rules apply to the state park you plan to visit through this link, **'DNR: Forestry: Indiana State Forest Recreation'.**

It is legal to forage for mushrooms off-trail in Indiana. Some experienced foragers may be able to guide you. They will boost your knowledge of discovering different foraging locations. Please see the following resources.

21 Country: Learn about Northeast Indiana's wild, edible plants (wpta21.com)

Foraging Tours and Classes in Indiana – Eat The Planet

8   Organized by Harvesting Season-45 Edible and Medicinal Herbs for Foraging

8.1   Introduction

The following sections are split into two main parts. The first part explains the actions of herbs. Actions refer to how herbal components act to accomplish a specific purpose. You will notice that herbs can handle multiple jobs. In fact, their 'job descriptions' are quite miraculous! The second part of the book provides a profile of forty-five edible foods and herbs called "Materia Medica".

Materia Medica means the study of the origin and properties of substances used in medicine. Each profile tells you: (1) the common name of the plant (2) the parts of the plant that are edible (3) the habitat the plant grows in along with botanical characteristics and identification techniques (4) the edible uses of the plant (5) any contraindications of each particular plant. It sounds like a lot of information. It is, but Materia Medica is systematic and meant to provide a reference point to return to again, and again. One may not always remember what is written, however, that is completely fine. Over time, by consulting the Materia Medica of a plant over and over again, it can become very familiar to you. The most important thing is to read the actions and contraindications of any herb you take before you take it.

Once you become aware of the actions plants possess, you can use them more confidently. Although the Materia Medica in this book covers many conditions one may never have, or encounter, you can educate yourself about various alternatives for care that exist. Furthermore, food is also medicine. When we know the nutritional value of what we harvest, it changes the way we choose, prepare, and consume our food. Foraging gives us the practical experience of utilizing the natural world to improve our health daily.

8.2   List of Herbal Actions

Now you may be asking, "Which herbs are for me?". Let's begin interviewing our herbs and discovering all of the jobs they perform so that you can find out what suits you best, and which plants you can find most easily, starting in your own backyard. The terms below are used in the 'Materia Medica' part where plants are described including their nutritious and medicinal properties.

Please note: *If you are already taking medication, you must consult with a trustworthy trained practitioner before taking any herb. It is always advised to follow the same advice when administering herbs for any condition.*

Adaptogens – These help various systems in the body 'adapt' to stress. Adaptogens protect, restore and strengthen. In many cases, they provide nourishment, just like food. Examples from this book include: Nettle, Oyster Mushrooms, Rose Hips, and Wild Garlic.

Alterative – Provides nourishment and strength for the body via removing toxic metabolic wastes (often from the liver). Examples from this book include: Blessed Thistle, Butternut, Burdock, Chickweed, Dandelion, Green Brier, Nettle, Purple Dead Nettle, and Sheep Sorrel.

Anesthetic – Depresses nerve function, thereby creating a loss of sensation or consciousness. This book only deals with topical anesthetics. Examples from this book include: Blessed Thistle, Plantain, Oak, and White Willow Bark.

Anthelmintic – Destroy worms and parasites in the digestive tract – Examples from this book include: Mugwort.

Antiemetic – Will reduce nausea and help prevent vomiting. Examples from this book include: Mint.

Anti-inflammatory – These work directly on tissues to soothe. They do not interrupt the practical aspects of natural inflammatory reaction, but they reduce the harmful effects of inflammation. Examples from this book include: Blessed Thistle, Birch Bark, Goldenrod, Meadowsweet, Pine, White Willow Bark.

Antiseptic – Destroys the growth of organisms that cause disease. Examples from this book include: Garlic Mustard, Oak (bark), Trout Lily.

Antispasmodic – This eases muscle cramping, as well as muscular tension. Antispasmodics include nervines that reduce psychological and physical stress (the brilliant design of nature!) Some antispasmodics lessen muscle spasms throughout the body, while others work with specific organs or systems. Examples from this book include: Boneset, Mint, Mugwort and White Willow Bark.

Antiviral – Prohibits the actions of a virus. Examples from this book include: Boneset, Garlic (wild or not), Milkweed, Prairie Moon.

Astringent – Astringents act to dry out a cell; they squeeze excess fluid from cells and carry unwanted substances out of the body. Astringents bind to mucous membranes. *Mucous membranes are the carrier of bacteria and the seeds of illness.* Astringents also break up fats and tighten tissues, releasing toxins. They assist with weight loss. They help break down proteins, reduce irritation and inflammation, and decrease fluid loss. Examples from this book include: Yarrow, Rose Hips, Oak Bark and Sheep Sorrel.

Bitter – These are exceptional herbs that have profound benefits. A bitter herb sends a message to the gut via the central nervous system. It tells the gut to release digestive hormones that stimulate the appetite, give rise to the flow of digestive juices and then increase bile flow. Consequently, the liver receives the signal to work more effectively with bile to detoxify and repair the gut. Examples from this book include: Chickweed, Dandelion, and Nettle.

Most dark leafy greens are also bitter. They are medicine in and of themselves. Befriend your bitter herbs wholeheartedly. Even though this category of herbs tastes bitter, remember that they clean the liver. The liver executes over 400 different functions. Three essential functions are blood filtration, metabolic stability, and nutrient synthesis. Hardly a person exists who does not need to optimize their liver function.

Carminative – Carminatives are rich in aromatic oils. They stimulate proper digestion, soothe irritations along the intestinal wall, reduce inflammation in general, help alleviate gas and promote easy elimination. Examples in this book include: Boneset, Dandelion, Mint, and Sheep Sorrel.

Cardiotonic – A beneficial herb that increases the strength and tone of the heart. Examples from this book include: Autumn Olive, Black-Eyed Susan, Butternut, Garlic (wild or not), Milkweed, Yarrow, and Sheep Sorrel.

Demulcent: Contains substances that soothe internal tissues. Examples from this book include: Mallow, Plantain (soothes both internally and externally).

Diaphoretic – Opens channels to detoxify and increase perspiration. In the case of bronchitis or chest tightness, it opens the lungs and initiates detoxification. Examples from this book include: Boneset, Butterfly Weed, Goldenrod, and Mint.

Emetic – *It causes vomiting*. Examples from this book include: Green Brier.

Emollient – Applied to the skin to protect, soften and soothe – Examples from this book include: Chickweed, and Plantain (soothes both internally and externally). Seaweeds also have mucilaginous or emollient quality although they are food.

Expectorant: An expectorant removes mucous or other unwanted substances. Examples from this book include: Boneset, Butterfly Weed, Mint, Mullein, and Nettle.

Febrifuge – This lowers a fever. Examples from this book include Birch Bark, Boneset, Prairie Moon, Yarrow

Galactagogue – Increases breast milk flow in nursing mothers. Examples from this book include: Nettle.

(A simple tea made from fresh parsley can dry up breast milk – the opposite action.)

Hepatics – Hepatics tone and strengthen the liver and increase bile flow. Examples from this book include: Dandelion and Garlic Mustard.

Hypotensive – This lowers blood pressure. Examples from this book include: Autumn Olive, Nettle, Garlic (wild or not.)

Immunostimulating: This action stimulates the immune system. Examples from this book include: Black-Eyed Susan, Garlic (wild or not) Prairie Moon, and Sheep Sorrel.

Immunomodulatory: This action modulates the immune system and stabilizes hormonal functions in general. Examples from this book include: Pine.

Laxatives – Laxatives stimulate bowel movements. Proper elimination is the cornerstone of good health. We should not have to rely on laxatives all the time to optimize digestive function. However, they keep us out of trouble until we address our deeper issues. We should consider all aspects of our diet instead of becoming too reliant on laxatives. Examples from this book include: Boneset, and Dandelion.

Nervines – Nervines tone the nervous system and are restorative. They are either nervous tonics that strengthen and restore, nervous relaxants that ease anxiety in the mind and body, or nerve stimulants that work directly on neural activity. Examples from this book include: Mint, Oatstraw, and Rose.

Nutritive – Nutritives contain high nutritional value by providing vitamins and/or minerals. Examples from this book include: Butternut, Ground Nuts, Oyster Mushrooms, Purple Dead Nettle, Oak (acorns), Pine, Purslane, Raspberry, Rose Hips, Serviceberry, Sheep Sorrel, Sumac, Thimbleberry, and Wild Asparagus.

Oxytocic – Stimulates uterine contractions and assists in childbirth – Examples from this book include: Nettle, and Yarrow (***On the other hand, if you do not want to stimulate uterine contractions, avoid***

these herbs. Of course, never use these herbs for self-care in this situation. Consult a practitioner.)

Sedative – Calm the nerves. Release stress and nervousness from the body. Examples from this book include: Oatstraw, Rose, White Willow Bark, and Violets.

Stimulant – Increases speed of physiological functions. Examples from this book include: Goldenrod, and Mint.

Styptic – Stops or reduces external bleeding by containing concentrated astringents. Examples from this book include: Black-Eyed Susan, Yarrow, Plantain, Serviceberry, Thimbleberry, and Cattails.

Tonic – Tonic herbs strengthen and revitalize a particular organ system or the entire body. Examples from this book include: Acorns, Blackberries, Ginger, Boneset, Dandelion, Green Brier, Horsetail, Pine, Nettle, Saw Palmetto, Rose Hips, Spicebush, and Uva Ursi.

Vermifuge – Rids the intestines of worms. Examples from this book include: Garlic (wild or not) Black-Eyed Susan, and Mugwort.

Vulnerary – Contains properties that heal wounds. Examples from this book include: Boneset, Blessed Thistle, Cattail, Chickweed, Forsythia, Mullein, Plantain, Serviceberry, Thimbleberry, Trout Lily, and Yarrow.

Once you become aware of the actions plants possess, you can use them more confidently. Although the Materia Medica in this book covers many conditions one may never have, or encounter, you can educate yourself about various alternatives. Furthermore, food is also medicine. When we know the nutritional value of what we harvest, it changes the way we choose, prepare, and consume our food. Foraging gives us the practical experience of utilizing the natural world to improve our health daily.

9   Foraging in the Spring

9.1   Wild Asparagus

Asparagus officinalis (3) (4) (5)

Parts Used: stalk

Actions: diuretic, nutritive, hormone-modu-lating, immunostimulating

Habitat and Characteristics: The light green spikes emerge in the early spring along sunny open meadows, roadsides, and fence rows. The easiest time to spot the plant is in the fall. Feathery adult plants rise to three feet tall and have small, red berries attached. Parts used, however, are the spring spikes.

Edible Uses: Consume just as you would regular asparagus. I like to chop mine up and put it into a quiche. Another option is to make an asparagus tortilla.

Contraindications: Asparagus seldom creates problems. However, if you have severe hormonal imbalances, moderate consumption is recommended.

Wild Asparagus Tacos

1. Cook a tortilla for less than a minute on either side.
2. Add some shredded cheese (optional).
3. Take it out of the pan and add some chopped wild greens and chopped wild Garlic or onions.
4. In a small pan, lightly poach the asparagus spears until they are soft and become even brighter green.
5. Roll them up in the tortilla.

9.2 Chickweed

Stellaria media (3) (5) (8) (9)

Parts Used: leaves, stems, and flowers

Actions: demulcent, emollient, diuretic, nutritive, alternative, antitussive, vulnerary

Habitat and Characteristics You can think of Chickweed as wild lettuce. Pick, wash and consume the aerial parts directly like lettuce and add them to sandwiches and salads. Chickweed thrives in mild climates yet can grow year-round. You can usually find it from May through September, sometimes in unlikely places like growing by the outside wall of your house.

Chickweed has a shallow root system and spreads rapidly. The stem is a prostate with multiple branches. It is straggly, usually four to six inches long, with fringe-like white hair on one stem. The leaves are extremely small, opposite, oval, and flat with hairy petals. The leaves have smooth edges. Its flowers are very white and small with a deep cleft, plus two parted petals. Use Chickweed when it is fresh only. It is too delicate to dry.

Edible Uses: Chickweed looks dainty; however, don't be fooled. It is an excellent herb for liver and kidney stagnation and detoxification, reducing weight gain.

Chickweed is most known for its emollient and demulcent properties. A simple Chickweed compress can soothe eye irritation and inflammation, heal wounds, burns, and abrasives. It is a powerful nutritional herb, especially A and C, a helpful restorative and nourishing herb for all systems.

Contraindications: Chickweed is a gentle herb.

9.2.1 Chickweed Smoothie for Weight Loss/ Appetite Control/Inflammation

Have a fresh start into the day with this tasty drink.

- 1 cup pineapple juice (pineapple is anti-inflammatory)
- 1 cup green tea prepared and cooled (green tea improves metabolism of fats)
- Two tablespoons of chopped Chickweed (Chickweed cleanses the liver.)
- One teaspoon of grated Ginger root (Ginger speeds up digestive function and clears the blood.)
- Two ice cubes (optional)

Combine in a blender. Take one cup in the morning and one cup in the afternoon.

9.3 Dandelion

Taraxacum officinale (5) (7) (9)

Parts Used: root, leaf, or flower

Actions: diuretic, hepatic, cholagogue, antirheumatic, laxative, tonic, bitter

Habitat: Any northeastern landscape without Dandelion seems unimaginable. You find it on lawns, between cracks in the driveway, and in rocky areas with poor quality soil. The leaves are multi-pronged and swordlike, coming up from a rosette base. The bright yellow flower has a multitude of short, thin, delicate petals with parallel edges. The flowers announce that spring has finally arrived and winter is over! It is a highly nutritional herb rich in vitamins A, C, B1, potassium, and minerals. The root of the plant has the ability to reach deep into the channels of the liver and clear them.

Edible Uses: The root depth is a clue that this herb can penetrate deeply into the channels of our systems. Consequently, Dandelion cleanses the ducts in the liver and kidneys in general. Its bitter action stimulates digestive function. Traditionally Dandelion was used to reduce fevers and stimulate milk flow in nursing mothers.

Contraindications: This is a diuretic. Take note that it can cause loose stools in the process of detoxification or diarrhea if it is overused.

9.3.1 A Delicious Dandelion Dinner

You can make an entire dinner with this plant! Here are some options.

1. *Pick the leaves, eat them fresh after washing, or put them in a salad or stir fry.*

2. *Fry the flowers after dipping them in pancake batter to make a fritter.*

3. *Last but not least, decoct one fresh tablespoon of the roasted root in a quart of water, strain, and drink as a coffee substitute.*

9.4 Garlic Mustard

Alliaria petiolate (8) (9)

Parts Used: aerial parts, leaves, stems (the young and tender ones), and flowers

Actions: diuretic, diaphoretic, antiseptic, alterative, nutritive

Habitat and Characteristics: Garlic Mustard is very easy to find and is one of the first herbs of spring. It grows prolifically in lowland woody areas in either shade or part sun. The long sturdy stems rise upwards with triangular to heart-shaped, serrated, light green, edible leaves that are soft to touch. The greens grow for three weeks before tiny clusters of white flowers emerge from the juncture of the stem and leaf. The flowers signal you that the herb's season is coming to a close, and after they bloom, long, edible, mature seed pods follow. You can still feast on the leaves and flowers. However, the stems will be too chewy in the summertime.

Edible Uses: This herb is an excellent source of Vitamin C. Leaves contain 190 mg of Vitamin C per 100 grams. By contrast, a hundred grams of orange only provides 53 grams of Vitamin C. Vitamin C aids in the synthesis of collagen found in every fiber of the human body. It scavenges free radicals and is a first-rate antioxidant. Overall, Garlic Mustard is an excellent liver cleansing herb. You can readily eat the leaves as you pick and wash them. Like Chickweed, you can spice up a salad or sandwich with them.

Contraindications: This herb should not be used by those with thyroid conditions because it makes iodine levels slightly fluctuate. For most, however, it is perfectly healthy.

9.4.1   Garlic Mustard Pesto

1. Combine a cup of chopped garlic mustard leaves with one tablespoon of chopped onion, ¼ cup of parmesan cheese, and ¼ cup of olive oil.

2. Blend well in your mixer.

3. Add salt if you wish.

4. Use as a sandwich spread or with any pasta or grain.

9.5 Jack in the Pulpit

Arisaema triphyllum (7) (9)

Parts Used: root, rhizome only

Actions: expectorant, diaphoretic, carminative, antispasmodic

Habitat and characteristics: Jack in the Pulpit is sometimes called Indian Turnip. It is found in deciduous woods and floodplains and requires rich, moist soil. It grows about six inches from a forest floor. Jack in the Pulpit has a very exotic look. The flower is unusual and rises from the forest floor from March to June. It has unique maroon and light green stripes with a spathe and a spadix. The spadix has tiny flowers embedded in it. Three oval leaflets span from the stem.

In the fall, its showy, bright red berries have the consistency of a ripe tomato and are an attractive food source for birds such as thrushes and rodents. The berries ripen in the fall and look like small tomatoes. Inside they generally have 1 to 4 seeds.

Edible uses: Jack in the Pulpit affects lung and liver. It is a very drying herb that is excellent for breaking up moving mucus. Another term for this action is *expectorant*. One can consume it for hoarseness and voice loss (also called laryngitis). For many types of coughs, it is also a beneficial herb. This herb is an excellent choice, from balancing burning and itching in the throat, to throat constriction, asthma, croup, and whooping cough. It works well if one loses the voice (a condition called laryngitis) due to excessive speaking and the root is decocted and gargled.

You can slice the root, cover it with a layer of oil and bake it just like a potato chip. Sprinkle salt and pepper on your chips after they bake.

Contraindications: Do not eat this plant fresh! Only eat the root after cooking or tincturing. Wear gloves when harvesting due to the calcium oxalate in the flowers and the berries. It might make your hands itch. Remember to pick the more well-developed roots.

9.5.1   Jack in the Pulpit Gargle for Voice Loss and Sore Throat

Make a standard decoction with one tablespoon of the fresh root or one teaspoon of the dried root in one cup of boiling water. Strain into a clean glass jar and mix with ¼ teaspoon of salt. Gargle with two tablespoons of this as often as needed. Repeat until problems resolve.

9.6 Mint

Mentha piperita (3) (8) (9)

Parts used: aerial parts

Actions: nervine, antimicrobial, analgesic, aromatic, antispasmodic, anti-inflammatory, carminative, diaphoretic, antiemetic, biliary

Habitat: Wild Mint is a common Mint family plant that grows in moist meadows and moist areas around marshes and streams. It grows from rhizomes (continuous horizontal underground stems with lateral shoots at regular intervals) and spreads by rhizome growth. The roots spiral around each other forming colonies. Full sun is preferred, but it tolerates partial shade.

The most striking feature of Mint is its smell. A similar smell is typical to the whole Mint family in one form or another. The average Mint leaves are small, equal-shaped oval leaves with slightly serrated edges. One distinguishing characteristic is that *the stems are square and often dark brown*. In the summer, look for long clusters of purple terminal flower spikes. The flower spikes have a small globe, a space, and another stem globe. In some wild varieties, the spiked terminals grow at the top of the stem.

Edible Uses: Peppermint (or any Mint for that matter) aids digestive distress, including nausea. If you get a stomach ache or headache while foraging, just eat several of the fresh, washed leaves. A standard Mint tea dosage would be the first line of defense for a cold, cough, flu, or headache. Use one teaspoon of fresh dried herb or one tablespoon of fresh leaves chopped per cup of boiling water. Take one to three cups daily until problems resolve. Mint is almost a 'one-stop shop' herb.

Contraindications: Mint is a very safe herb. However, if you accidentally rub the juice into your eye, it can sting.

9.6.1 Wild Mint Footbath

A Mint tea foot bath is incredibly soothing for the feet after a long day of foraging!

1. Infuse 1 cup of your fresh chopped mint leaves in four cups of boiling water. Let this sit for twenty minutes.

2. Strain and pour into a small tub full of warm water with a towel underneath.

3. Soak your feet for fifteen minutes.

4. Keep a hand towel nearby to dry your feet. You will feel significantly refreshed!

9.6.2 Creamy Wild Mint Salsa

This salsa will add a delightful, tangy taste to a foragers' meal.

1 cup of minced mint leaves

Two tablespoons of finely chopped red pepper

One heaping tablespoon of cilantro

½ cup of finely chopped wild garlic bulbs and stems

¼ cup of lime juice

One tablespoon finely chopped garlic mustard leaves and flowers

½ cup of plain yogurt

Combine all ingredients, run them through the blender and let them stand at room temperature for about a half-hour. You can serve these with root chips like Prairie Moon chips, Jack in the Pulpit chips, or Burdock root chips.

9.7   Oyster Mushrooms

Pleurotus ostreatus (1) (Please see the following reference[9])

Parts used: fungus head and stem

Actions: adaptogenic, antioxidant, immunomodulatory, nutritive

Habitat: Oyster mushrooms have a white to light brown or darker brown, even bluish-looking funnel-shaped cap. The flesh underneath the cap is white or sometimes a pale golden yellow. The gills are whitish to yellowish. The cap can grow from an inch to 15 inches. They have a short, stout stem and sometimes tiny cilia close to the base. They grow in rows, almost like tabletops, one above the other.

After a rainstorm in the mid-summer to early fall months, you may find Oyster mushrooms growing in a golden or brownish bunch on a *dead beech or aspen tree.* ***Learn to identify the beech or aspen tree first before you forage these mushrooms. Harvest them from these trees only as a beginner. If possible, check with an experienced mushroom forager in your area to determine what is most realistic and safe to harvest.*** They range in shape from flat and white to golden clusters. They fan out in multiple layers or tiny shelves from the trunk. The earlier you find them, the better. Oyster mushrooms are delicate and must be chopped and cooked right after seeing them. Rinse them thoroughly and chop them into small pieces.

Oyster mushrooms have been studied in cases of tumor inhibition and reducing high cholesterol. They have all of the same immunomodulatory effects as most other mushrooms.

---

9   Adam Haritan is a botanist who specializes in teaching mushroom foraging. Please watch his videos. They are excellent. *(20+) Watch | Facebook*

Contraindications: None are known—Cook all wild mushrooms for at least 25 minutes to kill unwanted bacteria.

9.7.1   Oyster Mushroom Saute

This simple saute is a delicious nutritional powerhouse.

16 ounces of Oyster mushrooms
Two tablespoons of olive oil
½ of a yellow onion chopped
Three cloves of minced garlic
Five green onions chopped
One tablespoon parsley (optional)

1.   Saute the onion and garlic first for about three minutes.

2.   Add the Oyster mushrooms and saute for twenty minutes.

3.   Turn off the burner and add the chopped green onions.

4.   Toss and serve alongside meat, rice, or pasta dishes.

9.8 Nettle

Urtica dioica (3) (5) (8)

Parts Used: leaves

Actions: detoxification, tonic, antihistamine, immunostimulating, adaptogenic, expectorant

Habitat and Characteristics: Nettles thrive in the sun to part shade. They prefer damp, wooded areas with rich soil or moist beds near water. The dark green alternate leaves are on the smaller side, ovate with a point, and have serrated edges. One prominent central vein with other veins fans out from the center. **You must remove the stickers from the leaves and stems before consumption. You accomplish this task by wearing thick gloves and grasping each sticker, giving it a slight twist and pull. It takes a little practice. Always wear gloves when harvesting this herb.**

Edible uses: Young, springtime nettle leaves are consumed right from the plant. First, you must remove the sticker at the point of the leaf carefully following the directions in bold above. They are also covered with light prickly hairs that irritate the skin. You must wear gloves. If you gather enough of them, you can add them to a salad like spinach. You can saute them or make a puree with onions and nettles to add to a baked potato.

Nettles are a superfood containing minerals, calcium, magnesium, potassium, iron, phosphorus, manganese, silica, vitamins C, B vitamins, and chlorophyll. They are perfect for immune support and reduce most allergic responses when you take three cups of an infusion using the leaves daily (one teaspoon of the dried herb or one tablespoon of the fresh herb per cup of boiling water. They support immunity, alleviate many allergies, restore kidney and liver function, and alleviate anemia.

Contraindications: Watch out for the stickers and cover yourself when harvesting. Please follow the recommended dosage. Nettles are a strong detoxifying herb. Detoxifying too quickly or without drinking enough water may cause headaches or nausea.

9.8.1 Nettle Leaf Stir Fry for Spring Liver Cleansing

2 cups of finely chopped nettle leaves (with the stickers removed using the method listed above)

1 cup of finely chopped green cabbage

Three chopped edible mushrooms

One clove of diced garlic

One tablespoon of grated ginger root

One tablespoon lemon juice (add ¼ teaspoon of lemon zest if desired)

1-2 tablespoons of sesame oil and soy sauce

1. First, mix the soy sauce, sesame seed oil, grated ginger, lemon juice, and garlic in your wok or frying pan.

2. Add the mushrooms and saute for five minutes.

3. Add the chopped dandelion leaves and cabbage and stir fry for three minutes.

9.9 Plantain

Plantago major (Wide-leaved Plantain) (5) (6) (7) (9)

Parts Used: leaves or aerial parts

Actions: vulnerary, expectorant, demulcent, anti-inflammatory, astringent, diuretic, antimicrobial

Habitat: You will find Plantain in sandy, rocky, well-drained areas. It thrives in sunny conditions and often grows between other weeds on an ordinary lawn. Most people regard this treasure as a nuisance.

This herb is widely available in vacant lots and waste areas or sunny meadows. Plantago major is wide-leaved with ovate equal parted leaves that fan out in groups or basal rosettes from the low base of the plant. You will see the basal rosettes during the early spring. The leaves have five deep ribs and are a little bit wrinkled. The leaves show five distinct lengthwise sections. The plant's stem rises from the middle with a dense spike of white and green tiny flowers that grow during the summer. The flowers mature into seed pods during the summer.

Its power to extract toxins, poisons, and even small objects from the skin is remarkable. Plantain acts as a gentle expectorant. Its soothing, demulcent quality is perfect for inflamed and sore membranes. It serves as a respiratory herb and can help soothe coughs and milder cases of bronchitis. It is ideal for children and more vulnerable populations. Its astringent qualities can help diarrhea, hemorrhoids, and also cystitis. Its most beneficial action is due to its styptic qualities that heal wounds. Plantain is certainly the forager's friend.

Contraindications: This is a gentle herb.

9.9.1 Plantain Poultice

A macerated leaf of Plantain used in the wild will soothe any small insect bite or scrape and provide you with an immediate antiseptic.

For wound healing, gently pack the Plantain on the area after applying antiseptic. Gather a cup of the leaves and chop them well. Place a hot steaming washcloth over the leaves and let it sit for at least a half-hour or preferably an hour. Repeat three times daily until problems resolve. It is best to use a fresh supply of herbs each time for the poultice. If you find that you have a short supply of this herb however, if the batch you use in the poultice is clean, you can use it a second time.

9.10 Sheep Sorrel

Rumex acetosella (9)

Parts Used: leaves, stems, and roots

Actions: anti-carcinogenic, tonic, astringent, carminative, immunostimulating

Habitat and characteristics: Sheep Sorrel is a great herb. It is from the buckwheat family and grows throughout the world in more temperate climates, yet also overwinters well. Sheep Sorrel has short, thin, light green leaves with one large lobe and two small ones at the bottom. They grow in a rosette in clumps that are usually no more than 6" high. The stem features maroon-colored lines and attaches to a creeping root system. The reddish stems match the maroon seed clusters that ultimately form at the top. The seed clusters resemble those found on their cousin, Yellow Curly Dock. Yet Sheep Sorrel is much smaller and creeps along the ground. Harvest the roots after three years of growth. You will know that the plant has been growing for about three years because the patch produced will be larger and the roots will look more well-developed, and a bit deeper. It takes three years for the roots to develop the most concentrated medicinal value.

Edible uses: Sheep Sorrel is growing in popularity due to social media. It is available, sustainable, and nutritious. Many people are now making green drinks with the leaves. The easiest way to consume them is right off the plant, eat one, and you will find it is pretty mild. Pick a handful to put in your salad. They add a marvelous lemony flavor!

Sheep Sorrel is another incredible super herb that is a medicine chest in and of itself. The green leaves taken in the form of a green drink will provide acid/alkaline balance. Improving your acid/alkaline imbalance will automatically improve digestion, constipation, bloating, and cramping. Interestingly, the leaves reduce sudden and ongoing pain and swelling of the nasal passages and respiratory tract and treat bacterial infections. So, it is another herb to add to the list for aiding respiratory distress.

In recent years the roots of Sheep Sorrel have been studied in cancer treatments. It is even listed as an alternative treatment on Memorial Sloan Kettering Hospital's website.[10]

The Ojibwa tribe in Canada initially worked with this herb. A nurse, who had breast cancer herself, began to work with this herb in 1922 after studying its properties with the Ojibwa. Her colleague, Dr. Chester Stock of Memorial Sloan-Kettering Cancer Center, later began to work with Sheep Sorrel roots. Dr. Stock, and the nurse, Rene Caisse, RN, used this herb with thousands of cancer patients over eight years with significant results. She collected a petition with 55,000 signatures to present to the Ontario Legislature, a testament to her tireless fifty years of working with these patients. It is worth reading the results of their research. Their treatments featured *Essiac tea,* which includes Sheep Sorrel root and eight additional ingredients. Because this is an

10   Please see the following reference: *Sheep Sorrel | Memorial Sloan Kettering Cancer Center (mskcc.org)*

advanced formula, it is best to order it and work with a holistic practitioner for comprehensive support. This book does not recommend treating yourself for a serious condition without medical guidance.

Contraindications: Consume the leaves as you would any form of wild lettuce. The roots, however, if used, have more vital properties. If you plan on using the roots for a severe condition, please see a practitioner who is familiar with this herb.

9.10.1 Green Smoothie with Sheep Sorrel

1. Place 1 cup of chopped Sheep Sorrel leaves in a blender with one banana and three tablespoons of yogurt.

2. Add ¾ cup of water and two ice cubes.

3. Blend until smooth and drink at any mealtime or for a snack. Of course, you can add even more value to this drink with ingredients like raw honey, Spirulina (sea algae) Propolis (a product made by bees), or Cinnamon.[11]

---

11   Raw honey is honey that is closest to its natural form and unpasteurized.

9.11 Wild Garlic

Allium sativum (5) (7) (8) (9)

Parts used: Bulb, flowers, stems, edible flower trail, and bulblets.

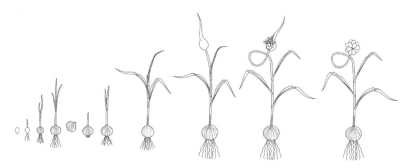

Actions: antibacterial, cardiotonic, antidiabetic, antibacterial, antiviral, antifungal, immunostimulating

Habitat and Characteristics: Wild garlic and onion generally grow in the eastern half of the U.S. Long narrow pencil-like stalk bulbs grow in clusters just beneath ground level. attached to the stalks. Flowers or

bulblets grow at the top of the stems from May through June and have a globe-like shape with tiny pale purple umbels. It looks like a small version of commercially produced chives.

You will find groups of light green stalks growing close to the ground in the earliest weeks of spring. Make sure that you leave ⅔ of each cluster in the ground when you dig the bulbs. You will find groups often one or two feet apart from one another in a colony.

Edible Uses: You can consume wild garlic in the same ways you consume a regular garlic bulb. However, wild garlic is more delicate when you roast it. Reduce the cooking time. Garlic is an excellent daily tonic. Eating garlic before working outdoors keeps insects at bay. They do not like the smell of garlic.

Contraindications: This herb is safe; however, wash it before eating it.

9.11.1 Wild Garlic Honey

1. Harvest two cups of wild garlic bulbs.

2. Cut off the green stems, clean them, and place them in a quart-sized glass jar.

3. Cover them with raw honey entirely and put a glass cap on the jar.

4. Let the mixture sit in a cool dark place for three weeks.

It takes time for the garlic bulbs to break down. However, they provide an excellent immune-boosting tonic and also lower blood pressure. Adults can take a teaspoon a day as a tonic or to ward off an oncoming cold or cough. For a more advanced cold or cough, you can increase the dose to one teaspoon every four hours. The honey provides additional antibacterial support.

9.12 Spice Bush

Lindera benzoin (2) (5)

Parts Used: bark, berries

Actions: expectorant, tonic, antirheumatic, aromatic

Habitat and Characteristics: Spicebush is a woodland shrub that sometimes grows along streams. It grows up to fifteen feet! Its branches spread and have a spicy odor when scratched with your fingernail. The leaves are bright green, thin and pointed. They are simple, alternate, and the deciduous leaves are two and a half to five inches in length and one and a half to two and a half inches wide. Flowers are small and yellow, forming clusters on twigs from the prior year during the spring. Flowers appear in early spring before the leaves. The fruits will appear in bright red, football-shaped groups in the autumn months.

Edible Uses: You can decoct the bark to treat colds, coughs, or loose stools from bacterial diarrhea (dysentery). When decocted as tea, the bark becomes a general wellness tonic. Compresses made with a strong decoction treat rheumatism. Dry the berries and grind them into a powder as an alternative to using allspice in your baking or savory side dishes.

Contraindications: The herb is mild.

9.12.1 Spicebush Stew

Gather the end twigs of the spicebush together and bind a handful together tightly.

First, make a vegetable stew with your foraged items. You can combine:

Two chopped potatoes

1 cup of nettles

½ cup of dandelions

1 cup of oyster mushrooms

1 cup of wild onions

(Bouillon or a salt substitute is optional.)

Combine these ingredients in a large pot and cover the vegetables with water. Drop the spicebush bundle into the pot. Bring all ingredients to a boil. Turn the heat down to simmer for twenty minutes until the potatoes are soft.

9.13 Trout Lily

Erythronium americanum (2) (4) (5)

Parts used: leaves

Actions: antiseptic, vulnerary, alterative

Habitat and Characteristics: In the early weeks of spring, you will find the trout lily sprouting in shady woodlands. Its long-pointed leaves are usually four to six inches and feature a 'trout like' pattern of maroon stripes and spots that resemble the brook trout. The leaves are three to five inches with a tapered point at the end, and two opposing leaves grow on the sides of the stem. The flowers are small and bright yellow with six petals. Six stamens extend from the center of the petals.

Edible Uses: You can use the leaves in salads or eat them alone. However, they may not be the tastiest leaf. Tea from the root will reduce fevers (1 teaspoon of the fresh root decocted for 20 minutes in boiling water). Trout lily leaves heal wounds either macerated fresh from the plant or made into a poultice. The leaves also heal skin ulcerations.

Contraindications: Consume sparingly, a half cup per day is plenty.

10   Foraging in the Summer

10.1   Black-Eyed Susan

Asteraceae (7)

Parts Used: aerial parts, seeds

Actions: vermifuge, antiseptic, immunostimulant, styptic

Habitat: The bright yellow Black-eyed Susan is found in fields, road-sides, waste areas, and ranges throughout North America. It is a bien-nial with lance-shaped leaves that attach to the stem. Bristly flowers are distinctly daisy-like and bright yellow with a raised dark brown center. Black-eyed Susan blooms from June through October.

The flower is very easy to find, actually unmistakable. Pluck the bloom, remove the petals, and roll the flower center until the seeds separate. You can chew on these seeds. They are slightly bitter. The root is easy to harvest, but remember not to pull up more than ⅓ of the total you find. Black-eyed Susan root tea is used for worms and also colds. Roots made into a poultice will treat sores, snakebite, and swelling due to edema. Black-eyed Susan has an immunostimulant action similar to Echinacea. The center of each flower has the same appearance, but the flowers are bright yellow not purple.

Edible Uses: Prepare one teaspoon of dried herb in one cup of boiling water, strain and take one cup of tea three times per day. You can eat half a teaspoon of the seeds three times a day, but they are bitter. For a less bitter alternative, please see the recipe below.

Contraindications: Wear gloves when harvesting, irritation is possible.

10.1.1 Black-Eyed Susan Seeds with Sunflower Seeds for Lowering Blood Pressure

Combine:

Seven tablespoons Black-eyed Susan seeds

Seven tablespoons of sunflower seeds (raw or roasted)

1. Mix seeds thoroughly with one teaspoon of a salt substitute for flavor.

2. Store in a glass jar.

3. Take one tablespoon daily to help keep your blood pressure down.

Sunflower seeds contain anti-inflammatory compounds, have reportedly lowered blood pressure, and are medicinal in and of themselves.

10.2 Blessed Thistle

Cnicus benedictus (3) (8)

Parts Used: Leaves and early-blooming flowers

Actions: circulatory, analgesic, alterative, immunomodulatory, lipid reduction, expectorant, respiratory tonic, carminative, biliary, anti-inflammatory, antimicrobial, astringent, vulnerary

Habitat and Characteristics: St. Benedict's Thistle, Our Lady's Thistle, Holy Thistle, or Spotted Thistle, is a prickly plant from the Asteraceae family. It is native to the Mediterranean region, from Portugal, France, and east onwards to Iran. Ironically, as is often the case with some of the most valuable herbs (like Plantain), this plant thrives on neglect. It is truly holy in that when no one else takes care of it, the Blessed Thistle can take care of itself and everyone else. It is not that easy to harvest but certainly worth the effort. It is also a very sustainable herb.

The plant and flowers are best harvested in the late mornings of summer months after the dew evaporates and the sun has risen. Blessed Thistle derives from the Latin term Cnicus benedictus. This plant scarcely exceeds 2 feet in height and has a coarse, erect, branched, and rather wooly stem.

The stickers grow on points around the leaf. There is more than just one sticker – so put your gloves on. Remember that just like Nettle you will have to pinch, twist and pull each sticker off the leaf. Or you can cut them off with kitchen scissors. The leaves are 3 to 6 inches long, more or less hairy, with margins lobed and spiny. The yellow flower heads, which appear from about May to August, are borne at the ends of the branches, almost hidden by the upper leaves, and are about 1 ½ inches long. Surrounding the flower heads are leathery scales tipped with long, branching, yellowish-red spines. The herb has an unpleasant odor that disappears after drying. Gather the leaves and the tops in late spring, just before the Thistle appears.

Edible Uses: This plant requires preparation. Don't eat it directly from the plant, especially if you are a beginner. Native tribes and settlers used Blessed Thistle to help cure the plague because it is both an expectorant and lowers fevers. One of the great things about this herb is its comprehensive benefits, and the plant is readily available.

Holy Thistle initiates a robust chain of reactions. First, it stimulates gastric juice production, and then it cleanses the bile ducts of the liver and gallbladder. Let us recall how many functions both of these organs perform. Remember that the gallbladder is a pear-shaped organ under the liver and on the right side of the abdomen. The liver and the gallbladder are companion organs. The gallbladder stores and concentrates bile, a yellowish-brown digestive enzyme produced by the liver. The gallbladder is part of the biliary tract. The gallbladder's absorbent lining concentrates the bile until the food digests. Then, the bile is released into the small intestine. *The benefit of Blessed Thistle is that it assists in this entire process. Plus, it cleanses the kidneys as well due to its diuretic action.*

Holy Thistle assists with liver detoxification and has been used to treat jaundice. One of the fascinating things about this herb is that it also treats melancholy and nervousness. When treating anorexia, both its nervine and carminative properties stimulate appetite. Holy Thistle helps improve blood flow. It is also used in formulas to promote breast milk production. Its antioxidant properties help the skin stay fresh and youthful-looking.

Contraindications: This is a potent herb. Please follow the directions for usage, and if you have a severe condition that requires comprehensive care, seek professional help from a holistic practitioner. **You must cut off the thorns before drying this plant or preparing it. The thorns may cause choking. Wear thick gloves when harvesting this herb.**

10.2.1 Blessed Thistle Tincture for Detoxification

Follow the simpling method, or the basic way to extract the herb's power. Make a tincture in a two-quart glass jar, cover two cups of the fresh herb without the thorns with 60 to 80 proof vodka. Let this sit for 21 days in a cool dark place. Strain and put into dropper bottles. For chronic conditions, take 1 inch or one dropper full three times daily.

10.3 Boneset

Eupatorium perfoliatum (7) (9)

Parts Used: dried aerial parts

Actions: diaphoretic, laxative, tonic, antispasmodic, carminative, astringent

Habitat: This plant grows in the Northeast and blooms from July to October. Boneset has a flat top of small white flowers, similar to Queen Anne's Lace, but they are more sparse and further apart. Again, the main thing to pay attention to is the **unique feature of the perforated leaves.** You will see how they perforate the stem. Hence, the botanical name, Perfoliatum.

Edible uses: Boneset is best consumed as part of a tea or other remedy and is not fresh. It is quite bitter. Boneset was a ubiquitous Native American and early European settler's treatment for influenza, fevers, liver congestion, and clearing the upper respiratory tract. When fevers and plagues rampaged their communities, Boneset was one of the first herbs they would administer. It is an excellent expectorant and subdues aches and pains promptly, especially from a fever.

Additionally, it will ease constipation and provide general detoxification. Muscular rheumatism subsides with Boneset, and it also tones the skin.

Contraindications: Please pay close attention to the botanical characteristics of this plant when harvesting so that you do not confuse it with Snakeroot. Boneset is safe, but Snakeroot is poisonous. The main visual difference is that the Boneset leaf is *directly attached to its long, main hairy stem*. No small stems span from the main branch and connect to the leaves.

10.3.1 Boneset Tea with Cinnamon for Joint Pain and Stiffness

Three tablespoons of dried Nettle flowers

Three tablespoons of dried Boneset leaves

1" of a Cinnamon stick

4 cups boiling water

Make an infusion with the Cinnamon, Nettle, Boneset, and boiling water. Drinking this tea will relieve aches and pains. Boneset is a plant with tremendous healing and rejuvenating properties for the musculoskeletal system. Use this tea for pain, swollen joints, and stiffness. This tea can be a tonic against aging fatigue and an excellent preventive remedy upon the first sign of fever or sniffles.

10.4 Forsythia

Forsythia suspensa (10)

Parts used: flowers, fruit, and bark

Actions: antiviral, styptic, vulnerary

Habitat and Characteristics: Forsythia grows in full sun, and you will notice the flowers with four bright yellow petals cascading on the tall thin branches as early as March. More than a hundred flowers grow on each branch. It is easy to spot as a border bush in the average yard. However, its medical benefits are hidden. The fruits appear after the flowers fade – look for oval and light brown pods. When you crack them open, they have two halves.

Edible Uses: Forsythia is worth exploring. Its flowers have a high antioxidant value and can be consumed right from the plant in spring. Add them to salads or use them to garnish anything! In summer, when the flowers disappear, they leave fruits. Use the fruit to alleviate chills, fever, muscle soreness, and internal parasites. You can make a poultice from the fruits to heal burns, cuts, scrapes, infections, and rashes.

Contraindications: Forsythia is a low-risk plant, however, don't take it before surgery because it slows down blood clotting. Do not use it if you are pregnant.

10.4.1 Forsythia Remedy for Flu Symptoms

Ease your aches and pains plus fever with this remedy.

1. Gather 2 cups of the fruit.

2. Let it dry on an absorbent surface like a paper bag or a large cotton cloth for two weeks.

3. Run the two cups of dried forsythia through a blender to grind the fruit.

4. Place the ground mixture in a two-quart glass jar and cover with the alcohol of your choice, 60 to 80 proof. Store in a cool, dark, and dry place for three weeks.

5. Strain and pour into dropper bottles.

6. Keep these on hand in case of flu and take 1 inch or one dropper full of the remedy four times daily to alleviate your aches, pains, fever and help you sleep.

10.5 Goldenrod

Solidago (8) (9)

Parts Used: aerial parts

Actions: astringent, stimulating, diaphoretic, diuretic, antiseptic, anti-inflammatory, analgesic

Habitat: There are more than 125 species of Goldenrod, most of them native to North America. Goldenrod was a scarce and valuable herb during the era of the early settlers and for native tribes as well. The English exported huge cargoes of Goldenrod during the 1700s and sold dried leaves to make medicine. Today, however, Goldenrod seeds proliferate. It is a prolific plant, spreading throughout the north. The term Solidago means solid. The medicine from it reputedly made you 'solid' or healthy again.

Goldenrod is an easy wildflower to find when it blooms in the fall. Its tall, sturdy stalks and dark green sword-shaped flat leaves with teeth alternate along the tall stems. Yellow rays of flowers fall backward in small bunches over the top of the stem from August to October.

Indications: Goldenrod uses vary from influenza, calming repeated colds, soothing bronchitis with purulent expectoration, or treating tonsillitis, sinusitis, and allergies. It is mainly a respiratory herb. Ironically, many people suffer from Goldenrod allergies. However, being introduced to a tablespoon at a time of the tea over the summer months can sometimes alleviate those allergies by the time fall arrives.

Contraindications: Do not take this herb if you have heart or kidney failure. It has a strong diuretic quality.

10.5.1   Goldenrod Remedy for Allergies and Colds

Combine 4 ounces of dried Goldenrod with 4 or 5 ounces of 60 to 80 proof vodka. Let this extract in a cool, dark place for twenty-one days. Strain this into a clean glass jar or dropper bottle when the extraction finishes. Take 1" or one dropper full three to four times daily.

10.6 Green Brier (Sarsaparilla)

Smilax rotundifolia (7) (9)

Parts Used: leaves, especially the shoots at the very end of the vines, and roots

Actions: astringent, alterative, diuretic, emetic, nutritive, tonic (leaves contain protein)

Habitat and Characteristics: Greenbrier grows low, so low that you might get tangled in it and fall prey to its long sharp thorns. Watch out! It has heart-shaped leaves that grow on vines that wrap around trees and other plants in shady forest areas. Notice the vines and the heart-shaped leaves divided by four or five prominent veins. Greenbrier is 20% protein!

Edible Uses: This plant is remarkable because it contains a much higher protein level than most wild plants in the Northeastern regions. Northern Native tribes relied on the high protein leaf from Greenbrier as sustenance, particularly while traveling. The Choke and Cherokee tribes used the root of this plant, known as Sarsaparilla, to treat skin disorders, liver problems, rheumatism, and excess hormones.

When foraging, gather the leaves. Eat five or six leaves as a natural source of plant protein. Remarkably, this plant also controls itching. Dry the roots and make tea with one teaspoon of the dried root in a cup of boiling water. Drink three cups daily.

Contraindications: Greenbrier (Sarsaparilla) has very tangled vines with sharp thorns. Please wear gloves when you are out foraging, but mainly when you harvest this plant!

10.7 Meadowsweet

Filipendula ulmaria (5) (6)

Parts used: aerial parts

Actions: antirheumatic, anti-inflammatory, carminative, antacid, antiemetic, astringent

Habitat and Characteristics: Meadowsweet or Mead Wort is a perennial herb that grows in damp meadows. It is native throughout most of Europe and Western Asia. However, for centuries it has commonly grown throughout North America. It is a stately-looking plant that can grow up to five feet tall. The dark brown stems are thick and crowned with a tip spray of tiny white flowers in a cone shape. The leaves are alternate, ovate and pointed. They are very dark green with purplish accents.

Edible uses: North American tribes used Meadowsweet as an excellent digestive remedy, effective for protecting and soothing the mucous membranes of the digestive tract. Native Americans introduced this herb to settlers. It reduces acidity and eases nausea; therefore, it is very calming in the treatment of heartburn. Its astringent quality helps decrease diarrhea. Meadowsweet does contain salicylic acid (the same substance used in aspirin) not as much as the White Willow, however, it still can reduce inflammation. It relieves fever, rheumatism, arthritis, and other joint aches. Put one teaspoon of the dried aerial parts in one cup of boiling water. Steep for 15 minutes, and strain. Drink three cups daily to reduce digestive discomfort, or inflammation.

Contraindications: Please follow the recommended dosage. Meadowsweet is an astringent herb. Drink plenty of water while you take it to rehydrate.

10.8 Mugwort

Artemisia vulgaris (4) (5)

Parts Used: leaves

Actions: vermifuge, emmenagogue, hemostatic, antispasmodic, diaphoretic, mild narcotic, bitter tonic

Habitat and characteristics: Artemisia vulgaris proliferate in high-elevation pastures, forest edges, valleys, hillside wastelands, ditches, and roadsides. The stems are branched and purplish brown. The ascending stems have short hairs. The multiple lobed-leaf version is widespread in the Northeast. The distinguishing feature is that it has medium-sized lobed leaves that are dark green on the top and papery white underneath. During the summer, small yellow clusters of cup-like flowers appear.

Edible uses: *Use only the leaves*. Mugwort treats liver, stomach, and intestinal problems. It is an excellent remedy for worms. It is also a noteworthy herb for controlling shaking induced by nervousness or insomnia. The tincture treats liver and stomach disorders. Mugwort is an extremely *bitter* herb.

Mugwort is applied topically in a poultice or taken as a tea internally to stop hemorrhaging or bleeding. Native Americans used it for colds, flu, bronchitis, fevers, and ceremonial purposes. Bundles of it are rolled and lit like incense for smudging in rituals and ceremonies. It has a musky, earthy smell when it is burned and is somewhat sedative. When Native Americans migrated to the Americas, they probably brought this practice with them from ancient Asia.

Contraindications: Avoid using during pregnancy and again, use the leaves only.

10.9 Mullein

Verbascum Thapsus (8)

Parts used: leaf, flower and root

Actions: expectorant, demulcent, antispasmodic, antitussive, astringent, and vulnerary

Habitat: Mullein is a striking plant. It is a biennial that comes from Europe. It thrives in turbid waste areas in part shade to part sun. However, it grows in full sun in waste areas or barren areas. It sends an impressive yellow floral spike up through a silvery green base of leaves. This plant grows on roadsides, sunlit gravel, or sandy areas.

Edible uses: You could call this herb the ideal family herb. Mullein is for bronchial and lung congestion; it is a gentle enough herb for children and the elderly. Often, it can ease lymphatic congestion. It is effective in dry, irritated bronchial tissues resulting from a consistent dry hacking cough, a respiratory infection, or smoking. It was a traditional remedy for tuberculosis and could calm the coughing spasms of the lungs.

The leaves are so sturdy and soft that they are called "nature's toilet paper." It is worth keeping an eye out for this plant when you are on a foraging expedition!

Native American mothers would use them just like a baby diaper. The plant compounds healed diaper rash directly. Native Americans sometimes made necklaces from the dried root for teething children to reduce pain.

Contraindications: Mullein is a very safe mild to medium strength herb.

10.10 Oat seed/Oatstraw

Avena sativa (4) (6) (7) (8)

Parts Used: fresh, young oat seeds

Actions: tonic, sedative, nervine, adaptogenic

Habitat and Characteristics: Oat Straw or Avena Sativa is very easy to find in open sunny meadows. It has a long stalk that can grow up to four feet tall. You will discover smaller stems at the top of the stem with long pointed pods at the end. Harvest the pods in early spring.

Edible Uses: Oat Seed or Oatstraw is a classic nervine tonic. Oatmeal has a similar quality, and many practitioners recommend oatmeal to ease anxiety. It is best to consume Oatstraw tea. Infuse one heaping tablespoon of the fresh oat pods you harvest in 1 quart of boiling water. To combat stress or exhaustion, take three cups daily.

Oatstraw gradually builds energy while reducing stress and is ideal for aging due to its tonic, nervine and demulcent qualities. It is beneficial for combating different addictions, including tobacco addiction, cannabis addiction, and even opium addiction. It uplifts you when you feel exhausted. Therefore, it helps with all the symptoms of burnout like anxiety, insomnia, weakness, fatigue, and exhaustion. Avena Sativa is exceptionally high in calcium and magnesium, two indispensable vitamins for supporting the central nervous system. It restores adrenal function.

Contraindications: This is a very mild herb when taken as directed. For restoration you can take it long-term, three to six months at a time.

10.11 Prairie Moon (Canadian Milkvetch)

Astragalus canadensis

Parts Used: young roots

Actions: antibacterial, antiviral, diuretic, immunostimulant, adaptogen, analgesic, febrifuge

Habitat and Characteristics: Canada Milk Vetch is found all over the U.S. and Canada. It adapts well to many areas, including prairies, woodlands, and stream banks. The Prairie Moon thrives in the sun to partly shaded areas. Its large white blossoms can appear almost like white lupine or a smaller version of foxglove (***Foxglove is a poisonous plant.***) The plant can grow up to two feet tall. Long stems fan out from the base with directly opposite thin swordlike leaves with smooth edges.

It is the perfect plant for bumblebees, butterflies, and honeybees to gather nectar, and it feeds wild turkey, groundhogs, rabbits, and livestock. Although generally not considered poisonous, caution is advised with any member of the Astragalus genus as they contain toxins at low levels.

Edible Uses: Harvest the root only. It is best to harvest the root before it gets too old and bitter. If the root is bitter, then wait to gather a younger root. In general, this root should taste sweet. When you harvest and slice the root, the plant should be four years of age and on the taller side. Since it grows to two feet tall, try to find the taller plants and avoid the smaller ones with underdeveloped roots. At this point, the roots, when sliced, will look like a tongue depressor. Most astragalus roots are long and circular, almost like a tube. You can chew on the roots to reduce pain, especially back and chest pain. A typical decoction of the root (1 tablespoon per one quart of boiling water) reduces pain and fever.

Contraindications: This root should taste sweet and mild. Do not eat the root if it is too bitter. The root is not poisonous in this variety, but a bitter root contains too many toxic alkaloids (or acids) for healthy consumption. On the other hand, if you learn to harvest the younger roots the plant is safe.

10.11.1 Prairie Moon Mashed Potatoes for Immunity

Four white potatoes chopped, either peeled or unpeeled

4 cups of water

1 cup of chopped fresh, young, Prairie Moon root

Three cloves of chopped garlic or a quarter cup of chopped wild garlic

1 cup of milk or a milk substitute

Butter to taste if desired

Saute the garlic in a medium-sized pot for a couple of minutes. Add the potatoes and prairie moon root along with the water. Bring to a boil and cook for twenty minutes. Mash the potatoes and then add the milk. Mash thoroughly or blend until smooth.

Prepare these chips to enhance immune function.

10.11.2 Prairie Moon Chips

You can slice the roots into the shape of tongue depressors and lay them out on a cookie sheet. Sprinkle salt and pepper on them and bake at 350 degrees for 15 minutes. Serve them with the Creamy Mint Salsa or the Garlic Mustard Pesto.

10.12 Purple Dead Nettle

Lamium purpureum (5) (7) (9)

Parts Used: leaves, stems, and flowers

Actions: alterative, nutritive

Habitat and Characteristics: Purple dead net-tle prefers rich soil, just like any type of nettle. It grows in full sun to part shade. Look first on your lawn; it might grow there. Clumps of edible leaves appear first that are heart-shaped with serrated edges and a purple tinge. The leaves attach to the stem with a short stalk. The pink to purple flowers are quite pretty, single tubular-shaped, and grow in circular rows around the top of this small plant. Leaves are opposing, and both the leaf and stem are hairy.

Edible Uses: Purple dead nettle is a treasure trove just like any nettle variety. You can use the flower in salads or as a garnish. Consume the leaves or flowers directly from the plant. Chop the leaves, flowers, and stems and put them in soups, stew, or casseroles.

Contraindications: It is always best not to over-consume any form of nettle. It is a potent liver detoxifying herb. A couple of tablespoons per person per day is adequate.

10.12.1 Purple Dead Nettle Salad and Salad Dressing

The whole plant makes a delightful complement to a salad. First, make the dressing. You will extract two cups of the flowers in a quart jar by covering them with apple cider vinegar. After three weeks, strain and make a typical oil and vinegar dressing. At this point, the vinegar will be dark pink.

Prepare the salad with a cup of chopped purple nettle leaves. Then garnish the salad on top with some dead nettle flowers.

10.13 Purslane

Portulaca oleracea (7) (9)

Parts Used: leaves, stems, flowers

Actions: nutritive, demulcent (soothing)

Habitat and Characteristics: Purslane is a creeper. It grows in poor quality soil, lawns, gardens, and sunny areas with gravel and clay. The sprawling purplish stems have alternate leaves with no stalk. They are thick, small, and paddle-shaped, almost succulent-like in quality.

Edible Uses: Leaves and stems are mild, crispy when raw, mucilaginous, and slightly tangy. They are high in iron and omega-3 fatty acids. You can eat the leaves and stems off the plant if washed. Or, you can chop them up and put them in salads. The chopped leaves make a delicious relish. Essentially, they take the place of cucumbers.

Contraindications: This plant is safe. Wash before using.

10.13.1 Purslane Relish

For a quart of relish, combine in a bowl:

3 cups of chopped purslane leaves and stems

½ cup of forsythia flowers, violets, yarrow flowers

Three tablespoons of wild garlic

Three tablespoons of chopped red bell pepper (optional but yummy)

For the brine combine, and heat on a medium setting in a saucepan:

1 cup of apple cider vinegar

1 cup of water

½ cup of white sugar

One teaspoon of salt

1. Put the relish mixture in a quart jar that you have warmed up with some warm water. It keeps the pot's temperature even and prevents cracking when you pour the brine.

2. Remove the brine from the stove. Pour it in the jar on top of the ingredients.

3. Pack the purslane down as you pour. Leave a quarter-inch of brine over the mixture.

4. Cover and let it cool for several hours. Afterward, put it in the refrigerator. The relish remains crunchy for a few days. However, it lasts in the refrigerator for a month.

10.14 Rose Hips

Many people have a Rosebush in their yard and yet are unaware that after the Rose fades away, a marvelous reddish bulb appears in its place that has excellent medicinal value.

Edible uses: Northern Native American tribes found multiple uses for Rose Hips. They extracted the juice and stored the herb for winter sustenance. Rose Hip tea provides a perfect ear, nose, and throat remedy for children and the elderly.

Rose Hips contain 4% vitamin C. The synergistic components of Rose Hips maximize Vitamin C absorption when consumed. Rose Hips scavenge free radicals with their antioxidant capabilities. They are anti-inflammatory, stabilize collagen, help heal wounds, and have been known to reduce tumors. Rose Hips elevate the white blood cell count, enhancing immunity. A simple tea made with dried Rose Hips is an immunity booster. Steep one teaspoon of the dried hip or fruit in one cup of boiling water for twenty minutes. Add honey to counteract the sour taste.

10.14.1 Wild Rose Hips with Lime Freezer Jam

1 cup of Rose Hips (trim them, cut each one open and then remove the seeds)

¾ cups of water

3 tablespoons of lime juice

1 ½ cups of honey

1 teaspoon of cinnamon

1 package of fruit pectin powder (1.75 ounces)

1. Combine the rose hips, water, lime juice, cinnamon, and honey in a bowl. Mix them together well. Either put them into a blender or use an immersion blender in the bowl to blend them well.

2. Pour the mixture into a small pan and begin to bring it to a boil. In the meantime, add in and stir the fruit pectin. Boil for only one minute at a rolling boil.

3. Cool the mixture and pour into small containers.

4. Put lids on tightly after the mixture has cooled and store in the freezer. The jam will last in the freezer for six months or longer.

10.15 Raspberries (Wild)

Rubus idaeus (7) (9)

Parts Used: berries, leaves, roots

Actions: antifungal, nutritive, anti-cancer, carminative

Habitat and Characteristics: Wild raspberries grow throughout the upper Midwestern and Northern regions through the Canadian border. The shrub has spiny branches with compound leaves with three to five leaflets. Watch out for this sharp-toothed bush. It has tiny white flowers with three or more petals and a prominent yellow center. Check the woods' fringes or the outer edges of fields for this bush. It may also be possible to find black raspberries in the wild, although they are less common. They will have the same characteristics, except that the berries are black, almost like a small blackberry. Harvest these berries in the late spring or fall months.

Edible Uses: After washing, the berries are consumed from the bush when red and ripe. If you gather the leaves, it is possible to make a tea that serves as an overall nutritive tonic (1 tablespoon of dried leaves per quart of boiling water). Berries, in general, are sour and astringent, an excellent choice for assisting weight loss. The berries contain ellagic acid, a substance that fights cancer. A decoction of the root made into tea will treat diarrhea or dysentery. You can add these berries to your usual pancakes or muffins! Delicious!

Contraindications: Use the plant parts as directed. In general, it is a mild herb.

10.16 Seaweed

(edible, all types) (11) (12)

Green Algae – Chlorophyceae

Red Algae – Rhodophyceae

Brown Algae – Phaeophyceae

Parts used: Outer parts of seaweed vary greatly. You must study exactly which type you plan to harvest in order to determine the part you will use.

Actions: demulcent, nutritive

Habitat and Characteristics: You'll find water-based algae in a very wide variety of colors, shapes and sizes. Look for algae along lake shorelines or edges of beds in rivers. Green algae grow most commonly in freshwater. Red and Brown algae is found in saltwater. All seaweed contain chlorophyll.

To start, you might recall having seen the most common types of seaweed in a health food store or an Asian grocery store after they have been dried. Perhaps you have taken chlorella, or spirulina as a nutritional supplement; they are seaweeds dried and ground into powder. The main plant part of seaweed is what appears like a leaf. However, seaweeds have one very large leaf that expands, ribbon like structures, or they look similar to the head of lettuce.

Algae is not a complex plant because it does not grow flowers, roots, or even stems as higher species do. Pigmentation amongst algae is quite striking. Color is the main feature of its identification and classification although within each color scheme there are thousands of varieties.

Green algae are the most common type of algae found and consumed. When it washes onto shore or when you see it floating in a pond it may not look very appetizing. Once you study, however, you'll discover the multiple benefits of Green algae. It is a primary survival food due to its' dense nutritional value. Manufacturers use Green algae for binding, to make paper products or pills cohesive.

Red algae sometimes look like a fern in the water. Its' colors include red to pink or violet to purple. It has a sheer quality and almost appears like a layer of plastic with ruffles or wrinkles around the edges. This group contains an astonishing number of species – over two thousand five hundred.

Green algae on rock (left), close up 'sea lettuce' (right) which is one edible variety of green algae. it can be used in salads and soups. Sea lettuce is also used to make ice cream, other food products, and medicine.

Close up red algae (left) used to make Nori sheets (right) that are widely used in Japanese cuisine.

Bladderwrack is a brown seaweed used in traditional medicine around the world. It is also known by the common names black tang, rockweed, 'sea grapes, bladder fucus, sea oak, cut weed, dyers fucus, red fucus and rock wrack,

Brown algae is usually brown to dark brownish yellow. This group features some of the thicker types like kelp, often reaching several hundred feet in length. Brown seaweeds might also have leaflike structures up to three feet in diameter. Sometimes this category uses a "holdfast", something similar to a root structure, as an anchor to rocks. Other types of Brown algae have rows of small air bladders. When they dry on the shore, you can pop them. However, in the water, the tiny balloon-like structures allow the plant to float.

Edible Uses: Mainly seaweed is safe for consumption however where it is harvested is extremely important. If possible, check with an experienced seaweed forager in your area to determine what is most realistic and safe to harvest. One must remember that whatever chemicals are in the water, feed algae. The cleaner and fresher the water, the better. There are so many species that it has been impossible to identify all varieties that exist and their edible potential.

Seaweeds are eaten raw, dried and put into soups, used as a salty seasoning or a thickener for jams, jellies, pudding or ice cream.

Contraindications: There are currently no known poisonous varieties of seaweed. Nonetheless, do not harvest seaweed in polluted areas. It absorbs poisons from the polluted water where it is found. Wash any algae you harvest thoroughly before you dry it.

10.17 Serviceberry

Amelanchier spp. (4) (13)

Parts Used: berries, bark

Actions: carminative, antimicrobial, vulnerary, styptic

Habitat and Characteristics: Different species of serviceberry range from small shrubs to trees throughout North America in sunny, open areas at higher elevations. One can think of them as a type of blueberry; however, they are different. They have a waving trunk, and the branches diverge. Its bark is gray, thin, and smooth. Leaves are simple ovate, light green, alternate, and pointed with slightly serrated edges. Small white clusters of flowers appear in the spring and have five slender petals, equally spaced and are about an inch wide. Once the flowers produce berries, you will find clumps of bluish purplish berries that look remarkably similar to some type of wild blueberries. They ripen in June and grow through September.

Edible Uses: Serviceberries have a very high yield if you find the right tree. You can eat them off the tree, but it is better to wash them first. Dried serviceberries as part of a trail mix are excellent food. Dry the serviceberries in a food dehydrator or on a cookie sheet at a very low over setting, 175 degrees. After you dry them, mix them with nuts and small crackers to make a nice trail mix.

Serviceberry trees provided sustenance and medicine for many Native American tribes. A tea from the bark helped women pass a baby's placenta following childbirth. The same tea alleviates stomach aches.

Contraindications: No contraindications apply. Different types of serviceberries have more taste than others. You have to find a tree that has the most flavorful berries.

10.17.1 Dried Serviceberry Cakes

Store these cakes and add them to your baked goods during the winter months.

1. Boil 4 cups of the berries until they are a soft mash.

2. Blend one cup of walnuts or almonds into a powder.

3. Add the nut powder to the berries and pour into well-greased muffin tins until they are about half full.

4. Bake slowly at 200 degrees until the cakes are dried.

5. It takes time, about 3 ½ hours total.

6. You can reconstitute the cakes by soaking them in water overnight.

10.18 Thimbleberry

Rubus parviflorus (4) (5) (9)

Parts Used: berries

Actions: styptic, vulnerary, nutritive, antioxidant

Habitat and Characteristics: Look for thimbleberries in damp ravines, near streams, and along the water's edge of a lake or ocean. Thimbleberries grow from the Northwest to the Northeast. The leaves look like Maple leaves, but they are a vibrant green, soft, with three different tips and serrated edges. The leaves are hairy on top and fuzzy underneath. The berries are very delicate. They form a red cap on a white globe underneath, and you have to pluck them gently. Put them in a secure container immediately, so they do not get mushy.

Edible Uses: You can eat these berries off the bush. Don't wash them; they will fall apart if you do. You can put this berry on your cereal.

Native Americans used to dry this berry and make cakes with it. Also, it was sometimes an ingredient of the famous native recipe "Pemican," a mixture of berries, animal fat, and nuts. Pemmican allowed Native American travelers to stay healthy and well-fed on long journeys.

Contraindications: This bush has thorns, so be careful. Fortunately, the thorns are not that large.

10.18.1 Pemican – a Traditional Power Food Recipe

Pack pemican into small containers for hiking and foraging expeditions!

Combine the following:

1. One cup of any type of wild berry
2. One cup of roughly chopped walnuts, almonds or sunflower seeds
3. One quarter cup of coconut oil (It congeals and binds the mixture together.)

10.18.2 Thimbleberry Fudge

This type of candy turns out like taffy. It has the same consistency. Depending on what you find, you can also substitute wild raspberries or serviceberries or mix them.

1 pound of thimbleberries

2 cups of sugar

Five tablespoons of butter

1. Lightly cook the berries in ½ cup of water until you can mash them.
2. Strain the berries through a strainer to isolate the juice.
3. Add the sugar and butter to the warm mashed berries.
4. Bring the mashed berries to a boil (measuring around 240 degrees with a candy thermometer.
5. Cool the mixture until it is warm.
6. Whip it with a wooden spoon for a couple of minutes.
7. Rub butter over a nine-inch pie pan.
8. Cover, refrigerate for half an hour, and then cut into pieces.

10.19 Violets

Viola spp. (5) (6) (9)

Parts used: leaves and flowers

Actions: purgative, emetic, antibacterial, sedative

Habitat and Characteristics: Violet flowers grow from the Mississippi up to the Canadian border in the Northern US. They have an irregular quality but are generally ovate-shaped. The familiar blue or purple violet has serrated, heart-shaped leaves. They are often found along the fringes of the lawn or beneath trees in shady areas. You may not have to look further for this herb than your backyard – how convenient!

Edible Uses: Violets are high in vitamins C, A, and E. Interestingly, the violet flower alleviates obsession!! The perfume industry has produced products from violets for a couple of centuries. However, it has excellent medicinal value. You can gather the leaves and the flowers in spring to add to your salad. The result is a delightful spray of purple. Like roses, violets, can decorate cakes or other desserts. Used as a garnish, they always provide a welcome contrast. The leaves have medicinal value when used as a poultice for skin abrasions. Like Plantain, they contain actions that pull toxins out of the skin to combat an insect bite or minor infection.

Contraindications: Only forage this plant when it is in bloom. Otherwise, you may confuse the greens with other leaves that are not edible.

10.19.1 Candied Violets (or Wild Roses)

Two tablespoons of high proof alcohol (like Everclear)

One egg white

White sugar

Whip the alcohol and egg white together. Dip the flowers in the liquid. Lay them out on a cookie sheet covered with parchment paper. Lightly sprinkle sugar over the flowers. You may want to fill a salt shaker with sugar. Then evenly spread sugar over the flowers. Let the flowers dry. The alcohol will evaporate, leaving the flowers with a candied coating. Use it to garnish whatever you desire. These ingredients will cover about two dozen flowers.

10.20 Yarrow

Achillea millefolium (3) (4) (8)

Parts used: aerial parts

Actions: diaphoretic, hypotensive, astringent, anti-inflammatory, diuretic, antimicrobial, alterative, hypotensive

Habitat and characteristics: Yarrow leaves are very delicate and fernlike; the stems are solid. The plant can grow up to two feet tall. The extremely tiny white, pink, or yellow flowers form in clusters that spread open at the top of the plant and the end of the side stems. The white flower variety works best for medicinal purposes. Yarrow grows in open meadows that are sunny and well-drained.

Edible Uses: After washing, eat the leaves and flowers directly from the plant. Yarrow leaves, and flowers are a perfect wild addition to a salad, soup, or stew. Yarrow is a superior diaphoretic for lowering fevers and controlling coughs. It is very suitable for children and the elderly. Please recall this important feature during cold, cough, and flu season. The gentle herb is a steady companion for all in the family. It also lowers blood pressure by simultaneously stimulating and toning the blood vessels. A simple poultice with Yarrow applied to a wound will stop bleeding. It is easy to see why Native American tribes widely utilized this delicate plant.

Contraindications: This plant is safe but, as always, do not over consume.

10.20.1 Wild Yarrow Flower Coleslaw

Here is a new twist on a favorite traditional recipe.

1. Gather ½ cup of the following and chop: Wild Yarrow flowers and leaves, Sheep Sorrel, Plantain

2. Grate 2 cups of green cabbage

3. Grate 1 cup of carrot

Combine and use a typical coleslaw dressing, salad dressing, or the Creamy Wild Mint dressing from this book.

11 Foraging in the Fall

11.1 Autumn Olive

Elaeagnus umbellate (3) (5)

Common names: Autumn Berry, Japanese Silverberry

Parts Used: flowers, olives (available in the fall), seeds

Actions: astringent, cardiotonic, pectoral, stimulant

Habitat: Autumn Olive is a deciduous shrub. Some consider it invasive. It goes by the common names Autumn Berry and Japanese Silverberry. However invasive it may be, one of its most excellent redeeming qualities is that it is *very easy* to find in many U.S. Northeast areas. You can spot it in the distance because of its silvery green leaves; they have a beautiful grayish green glow in the sunlight.

Autumn Olive will appear as a small bush, about three to four feet tall, or a short tree with multiple branches that can grow up to twenty-five feet. Wait for the fall to collect the tiny red berries. You can pick the flowers and eat them off the tree. However, it is better to wait and collect the berries, as you will see from reading the indications below. You can pick about a gallon of berries from some larger bushes in an hour! These sour fruits are also known as the "olives."

Indications: The flowers are astringent, cardiotonic, and stimulating. The fruit of many members of this genus is a rich source of vitamins and minerals, especially vitamins A, C, and E, flavonoids, and other bioactive compounds. It is also a reasonably good source of essential fatty acids. This characteristic is not common for a fruit. The fruits are consumed either raw or cooked. They are juicy but mildly acidic. The fruit must be fully ripe before eating it, otherwise, it is too drying *or astringent.* When ripe, the fruits make excellent jams and preserves. The seeds are edible and are small enough to swallow but are too hard to chew.

Contraindications: Do not ingest the leaves. They are somewhat toxic in larger quantities. Watch out for the thorns on the Autumn Olive branches! They are formidable.

11.1.1 Autumn Olive Honey as a Cardiotonic Remedy

Try this gentle and effective remedy to help lower your blood pressure.

1 lb of ripe Autumn Olives, rinsed, drained, and dried

4 ounces of dried Hawthorn berries (Purchase whole berries online.)

1 cup of raw honey (or any other high quality processed honey)

Two teaspoons of lemon zest

In a large saucepan, warm your honey. Then add the Autumn Olives and the Hawthorne Berries. Turn off the burner and let the honey cool slightly. Add the lemon zest, which acts as a preservative. Put this mixture into a large jar and store it in a cool place. The berries will extract in the honey as you store them for 14 to twenty-one days. It will turn a beautiful dark pink color—strain the mixture and place it in a clean jar. You can take one teaspoon of this three times daily to lower blood pressure slightly.

11.2 Butternut

(Please refer to[12]) – Juglans cinerea (4)

Parts Used: nut inside the fruit

Actions: carminative, alterative, nutritive, cardiotonic

Habitat and Characteristics: You will find Butternut trees in damp hardwood forests in the Eastern U.S. It is a member of the walnut/hickory family. Butternut is a medium-sized tree. It can grow up to eighty feet in height, however, it is generally half that size. Two to three smaller trees usually grow from the same spot. The bark is smooth on younger trees and has fissures with wavy ridges on the older trees. The bark is quite striking because of the fissure depth. In the winter, butternut twigs are reddish-brown with alternating buds that almost look like the face of a monkey! Butternut has alternate pinnate leaves growing up to seventeen inches or even two feet! The leaves are ovate and pointed with small serrated edges. The younger leaves are easy to spot in the distance because they are yellowish-green. The fruit is light green and egg-shaped or football-shaped. Its outer hull is moist, green, sticky and has a citrus smell. Butternut clusters contain three to more than a dozen nuts. So, it is a plentiful source of food.

Edible Uses: Butternuts ripen from late August through September. Gather the butternuts and remove the hull after gathering by positioning the nut vertically and hitting it with a hammer. Split and peel them. You will end up with two paddle-shaped pieces from each nut. You can eat them raw just like a walnut. Roast them at 175 degrees for an hour, and then grind them. Use the roasted nuts in baking just like

---

12   Clarke, John Henry, "*Materia Medica – Juglans cinerea*", *Juglans Cinerea. from Materia Medica by John Henry Clarke. Homeopathy.* John Henry Clarke wrote about the extensive medical uses of Butternut in 1902. A brilliant homeopath, Clarke did interface with Native tribes and adapted many of the remedies he learned from them for his patients.

walnuts or almonds. Sprinkle the rooted nuts on top of your cereal. Recorded medical uses include alleviating migraines, serious skin disorders, strengthening heart function, and relieving abdominal pains.

Contraindications: Wear gloves during all phases of preparation. When you strike the butternut, watch out for a liquid from the nut making sure it does not hit your eye. The liquid can sting.

11.3 Burdock (Great)

Article minus (4) (8)

Parts Used: root

Actions: alterative, anti-cancer, antimicrobial

Habitat and Characteristics: Burdock rosettes have two to five huge oval, wedge-shaped leaves with a heart-like lobe at the base. They are dark green with a wooly underside. The stems sometimes have a purplish tinge and remind people of rhubarb stems. The thistles are first green, then purple, and in the fall, they dry out and become a menace to any creature near them. Stay away from the burs and harvest the root.

Edible Uses: One of the best ways to use the edible root is to harvest the younger ones, perhaps a foot in length and two inches in diameter. Wash it well and let it cook into your typical vegetable soup. Chop various vegetables, including mushrooms, a few cloves of garlic, and then your chopped burdock root. Mix all ingredients well in a stock-pot. Bring to a boil and turn to simmer for several minutes. The burdock adds incredible medicinal value to the stew, almost like ginseng. It clears liver stagnation and supports healthy blood function.

Contraindications: Do not harvest this plant without maximum coverage. The burst of this plant will be almost impossible to remove entirely from your clothing or your hair.

11.4 Cattail

Typha latifolia (4) (5) (7)

Parts Used: shoots, roots, flowering spike head

Actions: styptic, antibacterial, vulnerary

Habitat and Characteristics: Cattails are unique. You will find them in swampy areas in part shade to sun. They grow worldwide; however, in North America, two species are common, the broad and the narrow-leafed. Cattails grow up to six feet tall. Their long slender leaves taper to a point at the end and are about two inches wide.

Edible Uses: Cattails are pretty versatile. The roots, new shoots, and the flower head are all consumed. You will find the white shoots with pale green tinges in the spring. Reach into the mud and pull them up. Peel the outer layers, and inside, you will find the tender part of the shoot. Saute the shoot. The flower head is effortless to harvest. Pick and then strip the bulk of the flower head into a plastic or cloth bag. Grind this portion into a flour and freeze it. It is loaded with protein, and interestingly, the cattail flour stays fresh for up to eight months.

One fast way to use the root is to slice it and place it on a wound or burn for relief. A tea made from the root has been used in Native American tribes to treat diarrhea, worms, and sexually transmitted diseases.

Contraindications: *Learn to distinguish the young cattail shoot from its poisonous look-alike, the Iris shoot. Cattail shoots are more round. Howev-*

er, Iris shoots are flat and hard. Cattail shoots have space in between each one, but Iris shoots grow in tight clusters.

11.4.1 Cattail Pancakes

Combine the following ingredients in a large bowl:

1 cup baking or pancake mix

½ cup cattail flour

¼ cup almond meal

Three tablespoons of ground flax seeds

One large egg

One tablespoon of lemon juice

1 ½ cups milk (Add a little more water if the batter is too thick.)

One teaspoon of baking powder (hopefully aluminum-free)

Mix the batter thoroughly and cook on medium-low heat in coconut oil or the oil of your choice.

11.5 Ground Nuts

Apios americana (4) (5) (6)

Parts Used: seed, tuber

Actions: nutritive (contain high protein)

Habitat and Characteristics: Groundnuts grow throughout the U.S. in temperate regions and wetlands (except for southern California and lower Florida). They climb like a pea vine and have multiple tubers along the length of the root. The leaves are compound and feather-like. You will find them on the edges of streams, bogs, and thickets.

Edible Uses: Harvest the roots or tubers from the early spring through the fall. Harvest the seeds all year long and eat them like peas.

Groundnuts were an essential food for many Native American tribes such as the Sioux, Cheyenne, Omaha, Pawnee, and Osage. The younger tubers that are not so thick-skinned taste the best. Cook them in the same way as a lentil bean or a potato. These tubers also make a perfect potato substitute and contain 15 percent protein. You can peel and roast them along with your wild garlic.

Contraindications: Do not eat them raw. Raw groundnuts interfere with protein metabolism. Always cook groundnuts.

11.6 Maple

Acer (5)

Parts used: sap from the tree, the leaves

Actions: antioxidant, anti-cancer, anti-bacterial, anti-diabetic

Habitat and Characteristics: Maple trees tend to thrive in northern climates. There are approximately 125 species, most of which are native to Asia, but several species also occur in Europe, Northern Africa, and North America. Maples can grow up to 130 feet in height. The smallest maple trees are less than 15 feet tall, with several small trunks originating from the ground level.

The most well-known feature of the maple is the striking color of the leaves. These leaves range from bright yellow to orange to dark burgundy in the fall. These colors signify the tremendous antioxidant benefits that this tree holds. Maple syrup contains many concentrated nutrients, which is why it is so valuable.

Edible Uses: An expert in medicinal plant research has found more than 20 compounds in maple syrup from Canada linked to human health, 13 of which are newly discovered in maple syrup. After his two-year study, he presented his conclusions at the American Chemical Society Annual Meeting in San Francisco.

Before the study, the Federation of Quebec Maple Syrup Producers knew that its product was full of naturally occurring minerals such as zinc, thiamine, and calcium. "We know that plants must have strong antioxidant mechanisms because they are in the sun throughout their lives," Seeram said. "We already know that berries are high in antioxidants because of their bright colors. Several of these antioxidant compounds newly identified in maple syrup are also reported to have anti-cancer, antibacterial, and antidiabetic properties."

Contraindications: Maple is a safe tree. However, use maple syrup with caution if you have any blood sugar issues.

11.6.1 Maple/Oak Leaf Massage Oil

1. Chop 1 cup of fresh young fall maple leaves. The younger and softer they are, the more quickly they will break down in the oil.

2. Chop or crush 1 cup of Oak leaves

3. In a clean glass jar, cover the leaves with 2 cups of either olive oil, almond oil, grapeseed oil, or jojoba oil. Let it extract in a cool dark place for a month.

4. Check on it periodically and shake the oil around a little.

5. After thirty days, strain into a clean glass jar. Use this massage oil as an emollient for soreness and inflammation. You can add fifteen drops of Eucalyptus essential oil to this after you strain the leaves from the olive oil. Apply it by massaging it into the skin as needed.

11.7 Staghorn Sumac

Rhus spp. (4) (5) (9)

Parts Used: berries from the conical head

Actions: carminative, antibacterial, antioxidant, nutritive

Habitat and Characteristics: Sumac is a shrub or small tree. It grows throughout the U.S. but not in zones with intense heat. It prefers the colder regions. Its main feature is a beautiful, crimson-colored cone-shaped flower and berry cluster. The leaves are lance-shaped and have multiple serrated leaflets on the edge. When leaves fade and drop to the ground in the fall, this bright red cluster becomes particularly apparent.

Edible Uses: Native Americans used Sumac widely. Gargles made from the berries soothed a sore throat, and tea from the flowers and berries helped digestion and alleviated stomach pain. The color denotes its antioxidant value. The flowers and berries can be dried and ground to make a tart spice for vegetables and salads. Steep the berries in hot water to make a drink that tastes similar to lemonade.

11.7.1   Sumac Lemonade

1.   Harvest two cups of the berries.

2.   Boil four cups of water.

3.   Let the berries steep in the water with one stick of Cinnamon until it has cooled. You can also add ½ teaspoon of lemon zest.

4.   Cool, strain, and serve with the sweetener of your choice.

11.8 Wild Mallow

Malva neglecta (7) (9)

Parts Used: flowers, leaves

Actions: demulcent (soothing), mild expectorant, antibacterial

Habitat and Characteristics: Wild mallows are a common plant that most people regard as a weed. It grows in fields, abandoned lots, barnyards, lawns, and gardens. You will find it in the sun to part shade, and it tolerates different soil types. The edible, alternate leaves fan from the stalk and have five to nine-pointed lobes. The edible flowers have five interconnected petals and are white or lavender with tinges of pink on the edges. Wild mallow sprawls and flowers in the late summer months.

Edible Uses: This plant is high in minerals, mainly calcium, magnesium, iron, and vitamins A and C. Gather the leaves and flowers for a salad or garnish. Otherwise, the leaves go well in soups or stews because they have a mild taste and do not overwhelm anything else.

Contraindications: The plant is safe as long as it is not overconsumed.

11.8.1 Wild Mallow and Garlic Omelette

1. In a small pan, saute one tablespoon of wild garlic and two tablespoons of chopped wild mallow leaves.

2. Whip two eggs in a small bowl with a tablespoon of water.

3. Pour the eggs into a small omelet pan and add the mallow/garlic mixture on top. Cheese is optional, but hard cheese makes this omelet quite tasty.

4. Cook the omelet in a shallow setting until puffy.

5. Fold it onto a plate and garnish the mallow flowers. It looks impressive!

12   Foraging in the Winter

12.1   Birch Bark

Betula pubescens (3) (8)

Parts Used: leaves, sap, buds, bark, and branches

Actions: antihistamine, diuretic, diaphoretic, anti-inflammatory, antiseptic, astringent, antirheumatic, cholagogue, febrifuge

Habitat and Characteristics: Birch is a deciduous tree. Over sixty varied species of Birch grow in temperate climates around the world. It usually grows near lakes and rivers in the shade to part sun. Birch trees will thrive in the cold. Northeastern environments suit them well. They colonize in bare, abandoned areas, and because of their luminescent bark, they stand out amidst a background of fading greens and browns. Thanks to their distinctive paper white bark, they are easily recognizable, hence the name White Birch. You will find places on the tree where this bark is peeling. Gather the leaves, the buds, and the peeling bark (but not too much).

Edible uses: You can make tea by drying the leaves and buds. Put one teaspoon in one cup of boiling water. Steep for 15 minutes. Take three cups daily for allergies or inflammation. Birch has medicinal benefits for osteoarthritis and rheumatoid arthritis. It is best to take breaks from this herb. For instance, one week on and four days off.

Smaller Birch branches are tied together to form a mini broom that is softened by steaming. After steaming the branches, according to ancient traditions, "switching" an inflamed area to release the Birch leaf essence for healing. **Do not try this method on broken skin.** A tea of the Birch leaves can cleanse the blood, muscles, joints, and kidneys.

Contraindications: Topical use is relatively safe as well as a standard tea decoction from the aerial parts. **Do not use the switching method on an open sore or wound.**

12.1.1 Birch Whisk for Arthritis

Gather several smaller branches and tie them together at the branch end to make a handle.

Soak this whisk in hot water for 15 minutes to soften the leaves and bring out their healing qualities.

Using a whisk in a bath or the sauna promotes better blood circulation and detoxifies the skin. The bather will prepare the whisk after dipping it in warm water or steaming it in a large pot for a few minutes. While in the bath, one performs a swishing motion with the whisk on the body. Do not apply too much pressure. The most important thing is to release the chemicals contained in the leaves.

Whisks release the chemical constituents of the leaves into the skin; also, they create a pleasant aroma. One can make them by binding together branches of the Birch, Oak, or Maple trees. All of these leaves have anti-inflammatory qualities.

Contraindications: Topical use is relatively safe as well as a standard tea decoction from the aerial parts. **Do not use the switching method on an open sore or wound.**

12.2 Oak

Quercus, spp., Faceae (5) (8)

Parts Used: leaves, oak galls, roots, bark fruit (acorns)

Actions: astringent, antiseptic, anti-diar-rheal, nutritive

Habitat and characteristics: Over ninety species of Oak grow in the U.S. Leaves are green, lobed, round, or pointed depending on the species. The more round-lobed leaves varieties, yield a sweeter acorn (White Oak, Burr Oak, Swamp Oak, or Chestnut Oak in the Northeast). Oak trees are easy to spot and generally have acorns on the ground beneath them. Acorns can take six months to 18 months to mature! The oldest living oak tree was two thousand years old.

Edible uses: Native American tribes typically cracked, shelled, and smashed the acorns, put them in a skin bag, and soaked them in the river overnight to release the bitter tannins. The river water would wash the bitterness away. You can blend them the following day and make something similar to nut butter. A decoction of the bark or root is used as a mouthwash to reduce canker sores or drunk as a tea to reduce muscle and joint pain or inflammation. Oak bark tea relieves dysentery and edema. It is a bronchial remedy as well. Take one teaspoon of the dried bark or root in one cup of boiling water three times daily for respiratory distress.

Native Americans commonly applied acorn flour as a poultice on sores or other skin conditions to extract toxins. Acorns contain the full medicinal benefits of this tree. Interestingly, many Native American tribes knew that acorn mush is one of the best foods to help a weak and debilitated body following an illness. Native American elder Dennis Martinez tells how his ancestors, from the O'odham and Chicano heritage, called the Oak "the tree of life."

Contraindications: Please stay within the recommended uses.

12.2.1   Baked Potato with Acorn Puree

1.   Soak a cup and a half of acorns overnight. Rinse them.

2.   Chop and saute one medium onion and two cloves of garlic.

3.   Add one tablespoon of chopped parsley and a couple of pinches of salt and pepper.

4.   Blend well to make a creamy sauce.

5.   Prick your sweet or white potatoes as you usually would. Bake for about 45 minutes at 400 degrees.

6.   Cool the potatoes slightly and serve with your acorn sauce over the top.

12.3 Pine

Pinus sylvestris (3) (5) (6)

Parts Used: needles, buds

Actions: anti-inflammatory, stimulating, tonic, immunomodulatory (adrenal balance)

Habitat: The Scotch Pine is a coniferous tree that came from Europe and Asia's great, mountainous regions. It is one of the most accessible trees to spot during the winter. Scotch Pine grows in full shade, up to one hundred feet. Long green, thin green needles grow in clusters at the end of branches. Pine needle buds attach to the base of the needle cluster. They are just as valuable to gather as the needles. The needles contain a lot of sap and branches, so wear gloves whenever harvesting. Gather the darkest green needles you can find. The younger, the better; they are the richest in plant constituents. Common pines such as the White Pine (Pinus strobus), the Western White Pine (Pinus monticola) and Sugar Pine (Pinus lambertiana) have edible pine needles bearing the same qualities.

Edible Uses: Pine needles and buds require preparation. Pine needle or pine bud tea is most common (1 heaping tablespoon of fresh needles and buds per cup of boiling water). Pine needles contain a fair amount of vitamin C and are high in antioxidants. Pine is anti-inflammatory. The vitamin C content of Pine needles tends to vary from species to species, and the younger pines tend to contain more. However, the Eastern White Pine needles in a USDA Forest study yielded between 0.72 mg and 1.87 mg of ascorbic acid per gram.

In one historical account of voyages from France to America, a French explorer Jaques Cartier in 1536, boiled Pine needles to remedy the scurvy of his crew. Guided by the local Iroquois, the crew recovered.

Contraindications: Follow the directions when consuming this herb. There are no known side effects. There are less-common pines that are not edible. These include the Yew tree, the Ponderosa Pine and the Norfolk Pine. Do not harvest needles from these varieties.

12.4 White Willow

Salix alba (3) (5)

Parts Used: bark

Actions: anti-inflammatory, antispasmodic, analgesic, sedative, styptic

Habitat and Characteristics: Its thin branches flow from the top, almost like a head of human hair. The leaves are lance-like with a gray-green color on top and a silvery-white color underneath. You will find this tree in bogs, open, damp, lowland wooded areas, or frequently at the edge of a pond. White Willow contains salicylic acid. This is a primary component of aspirin, and it is produced in a laboratory during the manufacturing process.

Edible uses: White Willow primarily reduces pain and inflammation. Traditional practitioners knew they could depend on it because they treated fevers with it consistently. That *which diminishes inflammation will also reduce a fever.* Central to Northern tribes used Willow Bark frequently for pain relief. If time did not permit harvesting the bark and preparing a tea, they simply chewed on a medium-sized piece of bark for relief. However, to make a tea, you would decoct one teaspoon of the fresh bark in one cup of boiling water. For chronic pain relief, start with three cups daily.

Contraindications: If you are already taking aspirin or another pain reliever, do not take While Willow at the same time. Taking both remedies simultaneously would double your dose.

Once you become aware of the actions plants possess, you can use them more confidently. Although the Materia Medica in this book covers many conditions one may never have, or encounter, you can educate yourself about various alternatives. Furthermore, food is also medicine. When we know the nutritional value of what we harvest, it changes the way we choose, prepare, and consume our food. Foraging gives us the practical experience of utilizing the natural world to improve our health daily.

13 Conclusion

This book has introduced herbs and plants in two contexts: one as food, and two, as medicine. We truly are what we eat, and we are also heavily influenced by the way we obtain and prepare our food. When we only shop at the grocery store, we typically do not place our consumption habits in a larger context. The holistic manner in which the world around us operates is forgotten.

Whether we are eating daily meals, trying to regain our health, or become even healthier than our present state, learning about herbs and foraging can help us. Why? It is because the air we breathe, the ground we walk on, the condition of the soil our food grows in, and the amount of sunlight we come in contact with all interconnect to create complete health. Herbs and plants, when used as food and medicine, have a synergistic effect on our whole system. When you look at the actions of herbs, like the ones , we are reminded that they behave synergistically. Every herb you will learn about is a microcosm of the whole. The parts of our bodies do not exist in isolation, and, neither do we. Thus, these herbs are presented to keep the big picture and long-term health in mind. Learning about these plants, even to prepare one meal, or to address one illness, is an important act of education, self-care, and hopefully preventative wellness. Let's recommit to a healthy lifestyle and remember, and revisit the words of this book, again and again.

Personal Notes

Sources

(1)   Meuninck, Timothy J., "Mushrooms of the Northeastern United States and Eastern Canada," Oregon: Timber Press Field Guide, 2017

(2)   Finney, Kevin, Director of the Jijak Foundation, "Foraging for Food," *www.YouTube.com*

(3)   Maude, Grieves, "A Modern Herbal" *A Modern Herbal (botanical.com)* 1931

(4)   Thayer, Samuel, "The Forager's Harvest: A Guide to Identifying, Harvesting, and Preparing Edible Wild Plants," Wisconsin: Forager's Harvest Press, 2006

(5)   Meuninck, Jim, "Edible Wild Plants & Useful Herbs" second ed., Connecticut: The Globe Pequot Press, 1999

(6)   Wisconsin Native Plants – Natural Heritage Conservation Program Wisconsin Department of Natural Resources P.O. Box 7921, Madison, WI 53707 August 2016, PUB-NH-936 Visit us online at dnr.wi.gov search "E.R." *MergedFile (wi.gov)*

(7)   Uva, Richard H., Joseph C. Neal, Joseph M DiTomaso, "Weeds of the Northeast," Ithaca, Cornell University Press, 1997

(8)   Gladstar, Rosemary, "The Art and Science of Herbalism," Vermont: Sage Mountain Press, 2014

(9)   Falconi, Dina, "Foraging and Feasting: A Field Guide and Wild Food Cookbook," New York: Botanical Arts Press, 2013

(10)   Gardener, Barbi, "Surprising Medicinal Benefits and Medicinal Uses for Forsythia," Outdoor Apothecary, March 18, 2021

(11)   My Canada, *5 Best Healthy Edible Seaweeds Grown in Canada – Find My Canada!* October 29, 2021

(12)   Nyerges, Christopher, Guide to Edible Seaweeds, Mother Earth News, *Guide to Edible Seaweed – Mother Earth News*, April 11, 2014

(13)   Donno, D., Cerutti, A. K., Mellano, M. G., Prgomet, Z., & Beccaro, G. L. (2016). Serviceberry, a berry fruit with growing interest in industry: Physicochemical and quali-quantitative health-related compound characterisation. Journal of functional foods, 26, 157–166. https://doi.org/10.1016/j.jff.2016.07.014

Rate us!

To support our growth

Positive reviews from awesome customers
like you help others to feel confident about
choosing my book. Could you take
60 seconds and share your happy experiences?

We will be forever grateful.
Thank you in advance for helping us out!

1. Scan with your camera
2. Rate us directly

Or

1. Sent us an e-mail to
   info@leafinprint.com with the subject
   'I want to give feedback'.
2. We will send you the review
   link as a reply

SCAN ME

We do all we can to ensure each book is
top notch. <u>Please let me know if there are
any problems or concerns</u> before posting
a review info@*leafinprint.com*.

Visit our homepage if you want to know
more about our work and our mission:
www.leafinprint.com

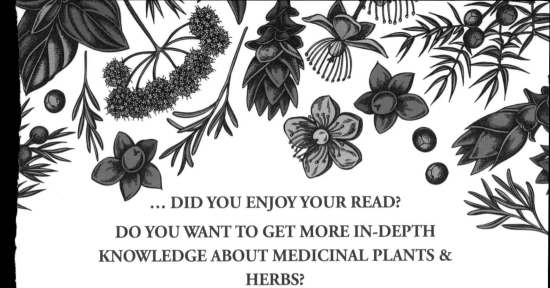

… DID YOU ENJOY YOUR READ?

DO YOU WANT TO GET MORE IN-DEPTH
KNOWLEDGE ABOUT MEDICINAL PLANTS &
HERBS?

From the same author

Herbalist's Guide to Native American Remedies

Medicinal Plants and Herbs, Powerful Herbal
Traditions and Remedies for your Effective
Home Apothecary Table

Check HERE:

www.leafinprint.com

or directly on Amazon:

*https://www.amazon.com/Herbalists-Native-American-
Remedy-Guide/dp/3907393015/ref*

Version v3 - 12.2022